Once Upon a Lyme...

Also by Cynthia Hamilton

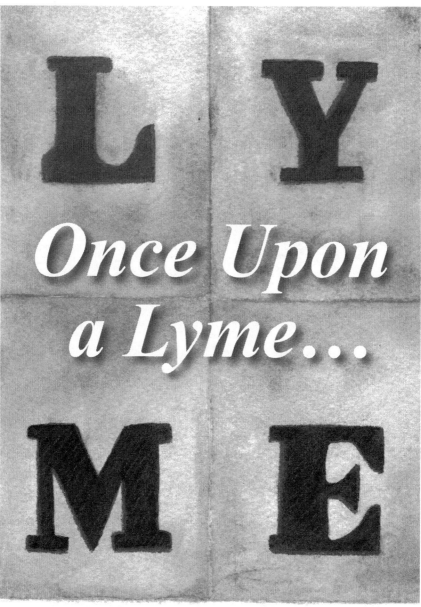

Once Upon a Lyme...

A Tale of Two Journeys

CYNTHIA HAMILTON

The events in this story are true. They depict my nine-year struggle with a nameless ailment that was finally properly diagnosed as late-stage Lyme disease in 2007. I'm not advocating any of the treatments or procedures that I've put myself through in hopes of getting well. I've written this book merely as a means of sharing what I've learned, which is that sometimes life will conk you on the head and hand you an incredible gift, all in the same stroke. The trick sometimes lies in recognizing the gift while your head is throbbing. This book is one example of seizing the gift while trying to mend a cracked head. Some of the names in this book have been changed.

First Published 2012
Woodstock Press

ISBN: 978-0-9904046-0-6

Editing by Gail Prather
Formatting by Six Penny Graphics
Cover design by Cynthia Hamilton and Deb Tremper

This book is dedicated to everyone who is battling illness, and for their loved-ones who often feel the sadness and frustration of not being able to make the illness go away.

Special thanks to Gail Prather and Deb Tremper for their expert guidance and support.

CONTENTS

Good News

"I'm afraid I have bad news. You have Lyme Disease."

"Oh, thank God!" I cried out, weak with relief.

"That's not the kind of response I usually get," Dr. Mesipam said after a stunned pause. I laughed.

"You don't know what I've been through," I told him. "It's a good thing it's not cancer—I would've been just as happy."

Don't get me wrong; I never wanted to be sick. But I was, and had been for a long time. All I was ever looking for was a concrete diagnosis and suitable treatment plan. All I ever really wanted was to get well.

During the nine year period—from the time I realized something was wrong, and the subsequent quest to Name That Ailment—I surrendered several times, swearing off doctors, their drugs and the endless tests. But the 'do nothing' approach can only go on so long. When the symptoms are so pervasive and debilitating, and your loved ones wring their hands and beg you to "go see someone," it's impossible not to do one's custodial duty.

It was this sense of obligation that constantly forced me back into the diagnostic arena. Until I received Dr. Mesipam's call, I had nearly a decade-long struggle, not just with the grab-bag of puzzling symptoms, but with the repetition of presenting my case to one physician after the other.

When Dr. Mesipam said the words "bad news," my heart sank. I was sure he was going to tell me the Lyme test was negative, and that I was no closer to finding out what was torturing me from within.

So, Hallelujah! I had the answer, finally. That was the good news. It was the only upside of learning I had a disease that, unless caught early, is difficult if not impossible to cure. When it has been allowed to flourish—and believe me, I did everything I could to make my body a spirochete-friendly environment—it's referred to as late-stage Lyme.

I can't guess how many thousands of people are suffering with the cornucopia of agonies that accompany Lyme. Because it is so difficult to diagnosis, many people end up like me, trying to battle an illness that already has a stronghold on our brains, organs, nervous systems, muscles and joints before we even know what hit us.

Unfortunately, I don't have any surefire remedies for fighting this disease. Five years after learning the name of my nemesis, I'm still chasing after an alternative cure, as it is widely believed antibiotics aren't effective in late-stage Lyme. I'm still on a quest, but at least I've ended the cycle of bogus diagnoses and useless prescriptions.

From this vantage point, I can look back and see not only when this journey began, but the surprising upside to this experience. I'm not talking about cherishing life more or becoming more spiritually aware. What I got out of my mystery illness was a new creative outlet, one born out of the fear of becoming bedridden. I can thank Lyme disease for turning me into a writer.

Bon Voyage

We don't always know when the course of our life becomes altered, but often there is a bellwether event that gives us a warning of what lies ahead. Technically speaking, I was given a tiny hint. It was so small, I completely overlooked it, dismissing it as only an insignificant annoyance in an otherwise happy day.

I discovered it on the morning we left for a three-week trip to Europe. At the time, I didn't give the bite on the back of my thigh a second thought, other than making a mental note not to scratch it.

After several days in London, I realized this was no ordinary insect bite. What started out as something so small you could barely see it quickly became very large and inflamed. We were about to leave London for the Scottish countryside, and we were lucky to track down a doctor on a Saturday. He diagnosed it as a particularly noxious spider bite. He gave me a week's worth of antibiotics and off we went.

Unfortunately, the drugs didn't faze it. By the time we left Perthshire for a rural village in Italy, the bite had become a painful, hard purple welt about four inches across, which soaked three thicknesses of gauze in less than three hours.

Our trip coincided with one of the most prolonged heat waves ever recorded. Everywhere we went the temperatures were in the mid-90s, and most the places weren't prepared for that kind of weather. The heat was so distracting, though it didn't take my mind off the huge dripping mass on the back of my leg, it did take away the will to seek out further medical attention.

Once back home in Santa Barbara, the monster on the back of my thigh started to subside, leaving only a large purple mark that eventually disappeared. But before the bite was gone, I experienced what I believe were two brain seizures: roaring in my ears, a slack jaw and a feeling of paralysis, followed by violent shaking from head to toe that seemed to last a couple of minutes.

I chalked these episodes up to the nastiness of the spider's venom, but decided to see my dermatologist anyway. As it was already healing, he concurred with the London doctor's diagnosis. I never gave it another thought unless the subject of spiders came up.

This incident occurred in the early '90s. Because of the experience, I became especially arachnophobic, killing every spider I came across with zeal, believing it was them or me. It wasn't until much later that I realized exactly what had bitten me. It was then that we were finally able to recognize that experience for what it really was: the onset of Lyme disease.

REALITY BITES

I have this superstition about European vacations: every time we return from one, we personally experience an economic downturn. After our 1994 trip, we went through a profound dip. In February of 1995, my husband put me to work as a receptionist at his mortgage company, out of necessity, not as a means of torture.

I've had two occupational phobias in my life: cooking in a restaurant and secretarial work. When Guy took me away from making mosaic furniture at home and put me in the front of his office, I had never used a computer and didn't even know how to type. I was petrified by the eight phone lines and the intercom system.

I had watched his previous receptionist manage her tasks with a mixture of fear and awe, as she would post the mail while simultaneously answering several ringing lines and taking messages, the old-fashioned way, with pen and paper. It was completely beyond my scope to imagine ever doing something like that. I suppose this new job was fate's way of preparing me for what was to come.

As business was slow, I bought a manual and taught myself to type. I mastered the phones, learned how to input loan files on the computer, took over some of the bookkeeping, and generally got the hang of office work.

In January of 1998, the unthinkable happened: Guy's office manager and main processor of twelve years quit. If our business had still been in the doldrums, that would've been one thing. But there had been a dramatic increase in new loans, and we were jamming. Her departure left us up shit creek without a canoe.

I became the office manager by default. But we still had two positions to fill, as we had been functioning with only one processor. We had perils filling both positions: a string of temps and unsuitable applicants, and hires that didn't work out.

To add to the mayhem, mistakes and oversights made by my predecessor would continually come back to haunt us, issues I was forced to resolve. It was sink or swim from the get-go, and I fashioned a passable if ungainly dog paddle. I had no choice.

By August, we had the staffing situation sorted out and we had hit a comfortable yet still hectic pace. Guy and I no longer had to work ten-hour days, seven days a week, but when we worked, it was flat-out.

We'd been so consumed with the day-to-day challenges of one of the strongest refinance booms in history, the positive side of dipping interest rates actually took us by surprise. Our once anemic bank accounts were now flush, and we were giddy with relief. There was an upside to the madness, something that made those anxiety-ridden months worthwhile. Gradually, we began to relax into a saner lifestyle.

The following January, we actually went to a movie. I remember this because we hadn't seen one in over a year, and because of the film we saw. It was *Hillary and Jackie*, the story of world-renowned cellist Jacqueline du Pre, who was stricken with Multiple Sclerosis in her twenties.

While watching Emily Watson's portrayal of the cellist, it hit me there was something not quite right with me. I know that sounds stupid, but even though I was aware of peculiar sensations throughout my body, the messages somehow didn't consciously register.

It wasn't until watching as Jacqueline began to experience the onset of MS that I had an awakening of sorts. Not that I suspected there was anything seriously wrong with me; I didn't, but I realized I had not been paying enough attention to my body.

Later that night, I took stock of the abnormalities that had cropped up when I was too overwhelmed to notice. Most of the symptoms I wrote off as too minor to bother with or attributable to just getting older. But I was sure the numbness and tingling in my hands and feet were something easily corrected. Thinking I probably had some sort of vitamin or mineral deficiency, I made an appointment to see an internist the next day.

To my surprise, numbness and tingling in the extremities is not an easy problem to solve. Instead of suggesting supplements, Dr. A sent me to see a neurologist on the third floor. The other issues I had dismissed as being trivial—the dizziness, chills, phantom pains and weakness—became little red flags of neurological disorders.

Dr. B put me through all the standard tests: MRI, nerve conductivity testing, spinal tap—in addition to seven vials of blood work. All the tests came back perfect, which would become a recurring theme in my dogged pursuit.

Dr. B, sympathetic to my growing list of symptoms, prescribed Celebrex, feeling sure it would alleviate the pain. Unfortunately, it did nothing. He sent me off to see Dr. C in Rheumatology.

Dr. C listened to my story, ordered his own blood tests, and also found nothing. Unlike Dr. B, Dr. C had a diagnosis: Fibromyalgia. He prescribed a drug to treat it. The drug didn't have any effect. He prescribed another; same results. As I could now add weird rashes to the roster, I went to see Dr. D in Dermatology.

By the time I got into see him, I had developed a bright red rash that flared out on both sides of my face. Dr. D took one look at it and immediately pronounced Lupus. He continued his perusal of my body, finding signs of "Lupus, Lupus, Lupus" around my nails, hands and arms. He sent me back to Dr. C in Rheumatology with his findings. The rheumatologist disagreed, insisting I had fibromyalgia, though it didn't quite explain the symptoms, nor did the medications help.

Around this time, a fellow student in my Spanish class suggested I see a friend of hers who was board certified in rheumatology and internal medicine and was an excellent diagnostician. What did I have to lose? I dutifully went to the County Health building, and immediately wondered why I was there. But I was propelled forward by the hope of getting some concrete answers.

Dr. E listened patiently to my saga, and ordered more blood tests. Everything told me to abandon this line of inquiry, but I disregarded my instincts. Two weeks later, I returned to get the results of the blood work. After waiting over an hour and being re-interviewed by an intern, Dr. E finally came in to tell me I was sleep deprived. I had no trouble sleeping. I was getting almost eight hours a night. I dropped his prescriptions for sleeping pills in the trash on the way out.

By now I was getting frustrated. How could so many symptoms not have a diagnosable cause? It was a weird situation to be in; I was now having difficulty walking, poor coordination, rashes, pains of every description—shooting, stabbing, burning—throughout my body. My skin, bones, joints, muscles and organs hurt. I was a walking pain blob.

Those close to me became concerned by my bouts of extreme pain and deteriorating motor skills. Everyone was on the lookout for someone who could fix me. Word spread of a "doctor" from China who had treated a friend of a friend's mother, and miraculously that woman, who had been confined to a wheelchair, was able to walk down the aisle at her daughter's wedding. I *had* to go see him. What did I have to lose?

This was another one of those situations where I should've taken one look at the place and bolted. But no, I didn't. This man was a miracle worker. Problem was, Dr. F didn't speak any English. There was also the little oddity of not having a plaque on the door with his name on it, or any name for that matter. I had spoken to a woman when I made the appointment, but there was no one else in this small, one-room office but the two of us.

Because of the language barrier, we skipped the preliminaries and he took my credit card payment of $250. Dr. F then led me to a massage table, saying what I understood to be "exam." He motioned for me to take off my top. He then had me lie down on the table.

"No, no," he said, then made the motion for me to turn over. I was not feeling altogether comfortable with the direction things were headed. So now, there I was, head in the face cradle, unable to communicate even if we could.

Without further notice, he began to attach several things to my back, which were not only painful, but also completely eliminated mobility. If the place had caught on fire, I couldn't have gotten off that table. All my muscles were constricted by the unknown objects stuck to my back. He then left the room for what seemed like hours.

I'd had only one other experience where I actually had to talk myself out of going insane. The other was the first MRI I had in the late '80s, where I was inside the machine for fifty-five minutes, without benefit of first knowing what the procedure would be like. I lay pinned inside the coffin-like enclosure, listening to the constant drumming and the occasional taunt from the technician of "DON'T MOVE!"

In both cases, I came very close to losing it. All I could do was talk myself through it, hoping the man hadn't abandoned me altogether.

When I was about to start screaming, the mystery doctor returned and removed the different-sized glass objects from my back. It wasn't until later that I learned I had been "cupped."

Back at the office, Guy was anxious to find out how the appointment had gone. I pulled up the back of my sweater and asked him if there were any marks on my back. His jaw dropped. "Whatever you do, don't look in the mirror," he warned.

Naturally, I flew to the bathroom to see for myself. It looked like I had a variety of cold cuts glued to my back—mortadella, salami, soprasatta. I was horrified. These lunch meats were as painful as they were ugly. I wasn't able to lie on my back for three days. I also didn't lose any of my symptoms.

At this point, I decided to try another rheumatologist. Dr. G was a kind, sympathetic man who I believed honestly wanted to find out what was wrong with me. I rolled up my sleeve and let the lab techs drain me again. Still, I appeared to be the poster child for perfect health. Everything he checked for was high in a good way or low in a good way. No anomalies at all.

Dr. G did, however, diagnose Reynaud's disease, which is numbness accompanied by discoloration in the extremities. This discovery didn't explain the other symptoms, but at least it solved the riddle of why my fingers and toes turn numb and purple when they get cold. Other than that and the rashes, there were no other visible abnormalities.

Even though he was stumped, Dr. G was not ready to give up on me. After several visits, the most useful idea he could come up with was sleeping with a pillow between my knees to help with the hip pain. As far as getting down to the source of the problem, his answer was spinal surgery, because it had done wonders for another patient of his. Finding his reasoning too vague to warrant high-risk surgery, I decided to go see our family doctor.

I had always found Dr. H to be a sensible, no-nonsense medical man. Over the years, he helped me with several aliments and had given me a physical or two, along with my annual flu shots. But during the time lapse between visits, Dr. H had gone New Age. He had traded his stethoscope and exam tables for mood lighting and comfy pillows; he had given up traditional medicine in favor of hypnosis.

After reviewing my paper trail of tests and doctors' diagnoses, he concluded there was nothing physically wrong with me; my problems were all in my head, which fortunately he could now treat. After all the dead-ends I had run up against, I was ready to believe I wasn't really sick, that all my pains and odd symptoms were imaginary. As he had been a friend as well as my physician, I decided to give his methods a try. What did I have to lose?

Four awkward sessions later, I was forced to admit this line of treatment was a waste of time (mine) and money ($200 a pop). Hypnosis wasn't the answer; my problems were very much real. Even after all the apparent proof to the contrary, I knew there was something wrong with me. And whatever it was, it was thriving.

Holy Toledo!

Every time we planned a trip, Guy would ask, "Where would you like to go this time?"

"Spain!" I'd say without hesitation.

In the good years, birthdays meant traveling. And being a considerate husband, Guy would always ask my birthday preference. But somehow, Spain was always vetoed in favor of another destination.

Finally, after 20 years, Guy decided he wanted to spend his 50th birthday in...Spain. What a great idea. Wish I'd thought of that. So, Spain it was: almost three weeks of traveling by car through the country I had wanted to see since I was a teenager.

Guy's 50th fell on June 1, 2000. As we planned the trip, I was still plagued by myriad symptoms, but had temporarily given up on the search for answers. By this time I had mastered the rash, having a succession of odd patches that continued to baffle the dermatologists.

I'm sure I'm forgetting some, but there are a few that stand out in my memory. The backs of my hands sported a very itchy red rash that persisted for weeks and just about made me crazy with pain. Another rotated from one eyelid to the other, back and forth, never on both at the same time. After a year and a half of putting ointment on it every night, it went away as suddenly as it began.

I had rashes on my knuckles, under my arms, and behind my ears. I had one weird patch on my left calf that lasted for years, and occasionally makes a comeback. I still had the "butterfly" rash on my face when I was feeling particularly sick or worn out. I saw it every night in Spain when I washed my face. All I can say is thank God for makeup.

As the trip approached, I developed a different rash on my face. By this time, I had lost faith in Dr. D, and sought help from a new dermatologist. It turned out that Dr. D had me using something on my face that shouldn't be used as he had prescribed. In essence, my skin had become addicted to this medication, constantly requiring more, even though using it irritated the rash. Dr. I took one look at my skin and had me stop using the cream immediately.

Going cold turkey caused my skin to freak out. My entire face turned tomato red. Frantic and on the verge of a breakdown, I went to see Dr. I the next morning. She calmed me down and gave me some products to soothe the skin and antihistamines for the swelling and itching. She assured me my face would be fine by the time we left for Spain.

In addition to the rashes, my legs were becoming less reliable, losing control of my feet and careening me into walls and doorjambs. They had also earned the title "Stockings of Pain" for their all-encompassing needle-dagger-spike-like sensations. All and all, I was in bad shape. But that didn't keep me from doing anything, especially not going to Spain.

As was usual when traveling to a non-English speaking country, I had to be the mouthpiece, or letter writer when making reservations in advance. But regardless of how hard I study, I'm no linguist. There were times when speaking in my mother tongue had become a challenge.

My lack of confidence with foreign languages added another layer of stress. And stress, as I was to find out, would always wreak havoc on my body. But no matter; faxes had to be written and calls had to be made. That was one hurdle; deciphering the return faxes was more difficult, especially if handwritten. After many attempts and a few disappointments, we had the itinerary set: six cities, six hotels. Nothing to it.

I wouldn't call us globetrotters, but we're definitely seasoned travelers. With all the time and attention spent on arranging our bookings, you can imagine how completely idiotic we felt when we got to our hotel in Segovia, after arriving in Madrid at dawn and riding the train for hours, only to find that our reservation had been canceled because we were a day late. Stupid. Ugly. Stressful. I don't know how we did it, but we screwed up. I think the one day stopover in New York threw us off. Whatever the reason, no one was happy.

We were fortunate there was still a room for us, especially since it was now pouring rain. Guy was so disgusted, he got into bed and slept till ten that night, which coincided perfectly with the Spanish dinner hour.

The next morning I had to get on the phone with the car rental agency and arrange for a pick-up a day early. That was fun, but somehow I got it sorted out. Even though we ended up with only a few hours in that charming city, we had to hit the road to be on schedule with all our other reservations.

We loved all the places we visited—Segovia, Toledo, Cordoba, Carmona, Sevilla and Madrid—but the trip definitely took its toll on me. There were a few more notable snafus, like wedging our rental car into the smallest, twisted dead-end in Cordoba.

But traveling abroad is about dealing with challenges. Looking back, I shouldn't have been putting that kind of pressure on myself. Shortly after we got home, I developed two new symptoms: stomach problems and a racing heart.

Figuring these new problems were unrelated to my other assorted ailments, I worked up my courage and went to see another doctor, a gastroenterologist. Dr. J ordered tests and concluded I had IBS, Irritable Bowel Syndrome. If you don't know this already, be wary of any diagnosis that ends in "Syndrome." It is a code word for not fully understood, explainable or curable.

As my main complaint was an acidic, bloated stomach, Dr. J put me on Protonix, a drug I would take religiously for six and a half years. It didn't do any good, in hindsight, but I was always afraid the problem would be worse if I stopped taking it.

After several months of tolerating the high-idling of my heart, the episodes became too annoying to ignore any longer. I wasn't worried that I was a candidate for a heart attack, but the 20 minute episodes left me feeling weak. I decided I should see a cardiologist, just in case.

At least Dr. K's tests were easy and produced instant results. I passed the EKG and stress test like a champ. The verdict: my heart was perfect except for something called atrial fibrillation, which was not life-threatening. I took the prescribed medication for a month. On the follow-up visit, Dr. K urged me to keep taking the medicine but admitted that it wasn't strictly necessary, so I declined.

Finally, I had two diagnoses that made sense and could be dealt with, more or less. All the other symptoms were still in high swing, but I had become too busy to be bothered running them to ground. Work had become very demanding again, and I was racing at full speed to deal with it all.

On top of the everyday work, I was studying to take the California real estate exam, a necessity for writing checks out of trust accounts and signing the broker disclosures. I was also planning a crazy but essential swap with our tenant in the front two offices of our condo. This would require dividing our space in two and completely uprooting everyone and everything—phone systems, computers, and every other piece of equipment and furniture.

As a reward for this extra aggravation, a wild seed of hope planted itself in my brain. I promised myself that after those two tasks were behind me and I had handed over our fiscal year-end statements to the accountant, I was going to sit down on my birthday and start writing my first book.

Story Time

On October 6th, 2000, I took the day off. I went into the office anyway, to sit in front of my computer and make good on my promise. After months of working on the story in my head, it was time to make the dream a reality. I sat there, like millions before me, staring at a blank slate, wondering how to make the first mark.

In the time leading up to this moment, I had practiced sentence structure and character development in my head while doing mindless tasks, like cleaning house and exercising. The more I worked at it, the more excited I became at the prospect of writing. I needed a creative outlet, one I could pick up and put down when pressing matters needed tending to, which was constantly.

Writing proved to be a good way to control the four-year-old who was forever chattering on in some region of my brain. I soon realized this voice could be put to good use in creating a real story, from beginning to end, and not just the incessant ramblings set off by the tiniest musings.

All my life I had been bombarded by this runaway narrative that sometimes caused me to yell *Shut Up!* I realize it's not wise to admit I hear voices, but I've been successful in harnessing that aspect of my personality and gainfully employing it through the discipline of writing.

I still have to put the kibosh on the prattle, but at least now I can sit this child down—figuratively speaking—and say, "Okay, we just finished the scene where Priscilla finds Tobias going through her notebooks. What happens next?" I'm now rewarded with an inner voice that has been trained to perform a task, a voice that actually can be quite well behaved under the right circumstances.

Now it was time for that inner voice to let it out, to put thoughts into words the way it had been instructed, to create a real story. I typed out two paragraphs and sat there staring at the wonder of it. It wasn't much, but I had kept my promise. That was the important thing. No need to go hog wild. Besides, I wasn't sure what to do next.

Satisfied, knowing once I started I would see it through, I let those two paragraphs stand as the beginning. On my following birthday, I finished the book. I was euphoric. I had completed a novel and it actually worked: beginning, middle, twists, ending—it was all there. I had proven to myself I could do it. Not wanting to let go of this new thrill, I started my second book the same day. I was on a roll now. But I'm getting ahead of myself...

Though my new secret endeavor gave me a mental and psychological boost, I was still on a downward spiral physically. Toward the end of 2000, I decided to have another crack at Dr. F, the third rheumatologist I had seen.

After pouring over the symptoms and the test results for clues, and nixing the idea of experimental surgery, Dr. F recommended that I see an endocrinologist, a friend of his who was particularly sharp at deciphering riddles. I had only a vague notion of what an endocrinologist did, but it seemed like a visit to a hormone specialist might be enlightening. What did I have to lose?

Someday I'm going to have to start trusting my instincts more. The visit to the Chinese doctor should've hit this point home with a flourish. But no; when I walked into Dr. L's office, I blithely ignored the fact that the receptionist was either the victim of time warp or a crazy person. She greeted me with a gasp of surprise, exclaiming, "My, what a pretty hair!" Her own was done up bouffant-style with a faux red velvet bow adorning the center, the kind you might find on a freshly groomed poodle.

After quizzing me about my hair care regimen in her odd, whiny voice, she informed the doctor of my arrival. After a short wait, I was ushered down the hall to Dr. L, the man with all the answers.

Somewhere in the back of my mind I must have been wondering why I continued to put myself through this charade. At this stage, did I really think I was going to find someone with magical diagnostic skills who could take one look at my chart and spot the obvious?

From the moment I sat down across from Dr. L, I knew this was not going to be the case. For one thing, he was a throwback to the Golden Age of Comedy, more specifically, Groucho Marx, making me his unwitting George Fenneman. Everything I said, he'd dismiss with a wisecrack, controlling the interview for his own entertainment.

Yet, I sat there as he interrupted every answer to his questions, breaking off to consult with another doctor about a mutual patient, as though it were a privilege for me to watch an extraordinary man of medicine at work.

Even this interruption was cause for amusement. As soon as he was off the call, he regaled me with his humorous take on the freshly broken hip of his 79 year-old patient who had fallen down in her orchard and lay there for hours because her 84 year-old husband was "deaf as a stone. *Deaf as a stone*," he repeated with glee.

By this time I was getting the uneasy feeling one gets when in the company of the mentally deranged. I actually wondered if this were some sort of prank that was being secretly recorded. Then I regretted the fact that *I* wasn't secretly recording it.

I had been sitting across from him for over an hour, and the reason for my being there had become completely overshadowed by this man's need for an audience. Dr. L was glib, boastful, condescending and impertinent. Every time I mentioned a symptom, he flicked his hand dismissively, downgrading its importance with some anecdotal comparison. I soon got the impression that every complaint could be explained away. I persevered, lining up all my abnormalities for him to shoot down.

Feeling a little desperate as I ran out of symptoms, I asked if changes in fingernails indicated anything medically. With a smarmy smile plastered across his face, he launched into the story of how his wife had long, beautiful nails when they met, and now they were short and split and she hated them. That was my answer. Many years later, I felt vindicated when my first alternative doctor explained what fingernails can reveal about one's health.

Having exhausted discourse as a means of finding the problem, Dr. L sent me off with his receptionist/nurse to get my height and weight. During this process, all doubts vanished: I had entered an insane asylum, and the patients were running the show.

It took Dolly five minutes to perform these two simple tasks. I am not exaggerating. I got on the scale and watched in disbelief as she pushed the weights to 200 and slid them in increments of a centimeter with painful slowness, pausing after each tiny movement to check and see if she was close to balancing the scales.

Exasperated by her ineptitude, I offered that I weighed 110 that morning, if that helped. It didn't. She was determined to press on. When she got the marker to hover uncertainly above 114, she scribbled the number in the file and went about the arduous task of measuring my height.

This was made especially challenging due to the fact that she couldn't have been more than five feet tall herself and could barely manipulate the measuring stick over my head. When she finally concluded that I was 5'4", I told her I had just had a bone density test at Dr. F's office, where they measured my height at 5'6". She was unconvinced.

"Look," I told her, "if I've lost 2 inches in 2 weeks, I think that would be significant, don't you?" She ignored my comment and led me into an examination room and told me to undress.

Now I was not only irritated, I was filled with an unnamable feeling of dread. Why did I have to take off all my clothes? Neither of those nut cases had mentioned anything about having a physical exam.

"So, you weighed a hundred and ten this morning, hee, hee, hee," Dr. L sniggered as he entered the room. "I guess you ate a pretty heavy breakfast this morning," he snarked. I had landed in a conspiracy of dunces. There was nothing I could do but long for escape.

Dr. L had me lie on the table where he commenced with an unannounced gynecological exam. I remember being stiff with apprehension as he continued his monologue. He'd ask questions, which I tried to answer, but I could only get a few words out before he'd preempt me with tales of his own trials.

One question prompted me to mention I'd had mono when I was 17, accompanied by tonsillitis and a sinus infection and a fever between 102–106 for two weeks, which caused me to lose 25 pounds and all my hair to fall out.

I didn't get past the word mono before Dr. L launched into a long, bitter story about being an intern and having mono and having to work ungodly hours and how nasty everyone was to him, and how nasty it was to work with sick people when he himself was sick. I could feel his anger as he dug around my insides, snarling at the memory of his ordeal.

He was still ranting when he snapped off his gloves, indicating my exam was over. He told me to get dressed. He left the room without any comment about his findings. I dressed and went to the waiting room. Another patient was called in; my visit had been concluded.

I walked out of that office without another word to the receptionist. I got into my car and burst into tears. I can't describe how demoralized I felt. I had been trying to find out what was wrong with me for 2 years. After two hours in that loony bin, I had been cured of ever wanting to see another doctor.

THE ROAD TO MANCHAC

In late 2000, we began to see business slow. After such a good, steady rally, it didn't come as much of a surprise. Being in a cyclical industry, we were used to the alternating periods of feast and famine, and because of that, I had learned how to navigate the company through the lean times.

The upside to the downturn meant more time for me to spend on my secret endeavor. As I had never written anything other than mortgage newsletters (you can imagine how scintillating those were), I didn't let anyone know what I was up to. I had never taken a writing class and I was taking a flyer at something that might've sputtered and crashed, or worse yet, might've been utterly unreadable.

Because of the uncertainty, I was happy to explore the act of writing in private. But when a computer glitch forced me to get help from Guy, I had to confess. To my surprise, he was very excited at the prospect and more optimistic about the outcome than I was. By then, I was far along enough to know I could string sentences together, and the story was already taking on a life of its own.

In the months before I started writing, I had become comfortable with the fundamentals of the craft—dialog, character development and plot—and I felt ready to tell a story. The only thing missing was the story. Hemingway said to write about what you know. This was a problem, as I didn't know anything remotely interesting. I was beginning to fear that after all the mental gearing up, there was no book in me, no story to tell.

One day in late September, as my self-imposed starting date drew near, Guy and I took a walk on the Ellwood Butterfly Preserve. Out of the blue, literally, came my inspiration. As I watched two hawks fly overhead, I realized I did have a story I could tell—a good one, at that.

What those hawks reminded me of was a eulogy of a good friend of ours who had been killed in a car accident in Mexico. Whether due to our friend's bigger-than-life persona, or our loss, I had been harboring a farfetched hope that he wasn't really dead, merely laying low until it was safe to reappear. I actually imagined him with a new face, living anonymously in some foreign country, hiding from...something *bad*.

I sat through his memorial service believing we were all taking part in the charade, though I was dismayed not to find any evidence to support my harebrained theory.

The reception that followed at his home did nothing to back up my case. There was a real sense of loss and grieving that I almost found annoying. How could everyone give up hope so easily? After all, they hadn't found his body after his car plunged off the cliff. Could I be the only one who found the circumstances suspicious? Our colorful friend was not one to have his life extinguished by a car accident in some hokey little village in Mexico. Surely this had to be a ruse.

Wisely, I didn't share my speculations with anyone else, but I did do a great deal of observing, learning details that, during our walk on Elwood, would turn into good fodder for a novel. Eureka, I thought: I had a story.

Not wanting to draw any parallels between our friend and the character in my book, I relocated the story to New Orleans, a place I knew well, a place that naturally lends itself to tales of suspicious death and disappearance. Immediately, the whole scenario began to blossom in my head.

Once I started writing, the situations and the characters just presented themselves. I had a ball weaving my protagonist through a web of bizarre circumstances and eccentric characters, against the atmospheric backdrop of the French Quarter, Uptown New Orleans and the surrounding parishes.

Guy became my facilitator, making dinner while I stole an hour of writing time, proof-reading chapters as I finished them. Because my secrecy pact had been broken, I starting sending chapters to my mother-in-law, Elena, who lived in New Orleans. She was thrilled by my efforts, if for no other reasons than she loved to read and was steadfastly supportive of anything I did. I told my sister at some point, but other than that, no one else knew what I was doing.

About a third of the way through the book, I needed to do some firsthand exploring, which necessitated a trip to N.O. I had concocted a dramatic scene where the protagonist, Audrey Dupree, becomes bonded to the cavalier Blaze Dixon through a tragic incident on the highway to the tiny town of Manchac.

It was a very complicated scene requiring certain elements to be present. Even though this was a work of fiction, I had a notion the backdrop of this accounting had to be accurate. In any event, it was a good excuse to make the trip, back to my husband's hometown and the place we had lived together for almost two years.

In this flashback, Blaze has left the bar Audrey has been tending, only to show up again after closing, his clothes disheveled and bloody, his car showing signs of a collision. Against her better judgment, Audrey lets him in and listens to his horrific account of hitting a girl on a bicycle. After admitting he doesn't know if she's alive or dead, he convinces Audrey to drive him back to Manchac in her car.

Because this scene could only happen on a road with specific features, I wanted to be sure if my memory of the drive from New Orleans to Manchac would fit the bill. So, off we went, looking for the scene of a fictional crime.

The closer we got to Manchac, the more I doubted my memory. We started brainstorming, trying to figure out what other place I could've been thinking of, or what other locale might work instead.

We reached Manchac, a town the size of a speck on the map, without finding the landmarks I had been looking for. We made a U-turn and headed back. Right away, things began to fall into place: everything was there, just the way I had envisioned it. The change in direction had made unseen markers visible, exactly as I had written it. I was elated.

We drove to La Place to make sure I had the lay of that town right. It had every landmark I needed, from the truck stop where Audrey seeks directions, to the location of the hospital. Everything was as I had imagined it.

Halfway through the book, a strange thing happened. Before I started writing it, I knew how it would end. I had the whole thing figured out, and I was dead-set on a certain ending, the only one that seemed right. But I came to a crossroads and I discovered something: if you create characters that ring true, you can't compel them do something that goes against their nature. If you force them, you compromise the integrity of the story.

So, in the middle of the book, the plot took a dramatic turn, one dictated by the dead guy. Everything changed from that point and I wrote without a mental map, only a new destination in mind. But in the end, it worked and made for a more interesting, unexpected tale. I was grateful I had the sense to listen to the players and not force my will on them.

Because I was a novice, I believed—despite drawing a kernel of inspiration from an actual event—that *The Road to Manchac* was entirely a work of fiction. I actually insisted the book was in no way autobiographical, somehow overlooking the fact that the protagonist lived in the same building we did in the French Quarter, and that my mother-in-law, her cleaning lady, two of my best friends, and our cat had fairly prominent roles.

I laughed out loud some years later when it became patently obvious to me what I had done. I suppose I had subconsciously clung to Hemingway's advice and wrote about personalities I knew well, though I completely modified the identity of the central character, shielding his memory from the outrageous deeds of his alter ego.

By contrast, the second book, *Less than Perfect,* was cut entirely from whole cloth. Originally titled *Microcosm,* the story takes place in a high-rise building in L.A. There are four main characters, all of whom work in The Paragon Plaza. The building itself is the catalyst to the relationships that develop, intersecting four individuals from completely different backgrounds.

Madeline Spears met her soon-to-be-ex, Adam in the ground floor deli some years before the story begins. She is a regional manager of a national clothing retailer. Adam is the driving force behind The Symington Group, a powerhouse branding agency. Grace is the beautiful hostess in the plaza-level café and a closet-case cellist. And Jason is a deliberately underachieving clerk at Planet Video on the lower ground level. Each of these characters wears a placid veneer that covers a painful past.

As their paths entwine, their pasts become their unraveling, forcing them to confront their demons head on. Though there are tragic elements to the story, the supporting characters and the odd alliances of the main foursome produce an over-all comic effect.

As I have discovered in subsequent novels, I just don't 'see' straight drama. I don't think I'm capable of writing a heavy, tear-jerking saga where everyone is serious and the action centers on tragedy. For me, humor is part of everyday life; no matter how dismal it gets, there's always some bit of hilarity to keep us off that bridge.

The inspiration for *Less than Perfect* came from uneventful encounters with our local video clerk. There was nothing special about our interactions. He was young, aloof and not especially thrilled with his job. Other than that, I knew nothing about him. But there was something in his demeanor that spawned an entire book.

As would happen with four out of the five novels I've written to date, the character who initially sparked my imagination would yield the center stage to another player, in this case taking an equal role in the ensemble. Because of the four individual story plots, this book was longer and not finished by my next birthday. It took me a year and a half to finish it, and during that time, many important changes occurred, changes that would alter the course of our lives.

Too Much to Hope For

O n January 15th, 2002, it was déjà vu all over again. A loan agent gave his resignation and left to open his own mortgage company, taking our loan processor with him. Fortunately, this time we had a back-up, one who turned out to be superior in every way, and who would become like a member of our family.

Leah easily segued into her role of main processor, learning everything on the fly she didn't already know. Rates were dropping, and before we knew it, we were in a stronger refi-frenzy than the previous one. After the brief upheaval, we were right back on course, with a smaller, more efficient crew, and a whole lot less drama.

A couple of weeks after the staffing change-up, Guy emailed me a listing from MLS of a 20 acre property in Santa Ynez with horse facilities and a small, barn-style guesthouse. It gave me a sharp pang because it was exactly what we wanted out of our nine acres of dirt in neighboring Los Olivos.

We had owned our property for a few years, and during that time we had plans drawn up for a beautiful hacienda-style home. I drew up my vision of the house, then the architect added his touches and did all the drawings. We staked the property and planned the landscaping, some of which we'd put in before breaking ground. We were very excited. Problem was, every time we met, the estimated cost would jump up another hundred-grand.

When the price tag reached $750,000, Guy and I decided a plan B was in order. Gone were the grandiose visions of an elegant bar at one end of the house, the walled-in secret garden off the master wing, and the interior patio, which offered a shaded veranda on three sides, fountain, built-in barbeque, and fireplace.

Plan B consisted of a barn with an 800 sq. ft. apartment. I drew up the plans, utilizing some of the barn space for necessities that wouldn't fit in the apartment. By the time we factored in all the infrastructure costs—driveway from main road, water and power to the site—we were looking at spending 250K.

The whole idea started seeming less appealing, especially to me. After all, we already had a house we loved in Summerland, and Guy had finally gotten the message that we weren't selling that to move to the Valley. Still, he pined for a place up there. He started dragging me to every open house in the million dollar range, for what purpose, I couldn't fathom.

At some point, Guy confided in a friend his desire to buy a property with a house already in place. Ted said if we did that, he'd buy our property, which was adjacent to the Brander Vineyard, maker of his favorite wine.

I guess I didn't really put much stock in the idea: it just seemed too much to hope for. So, when Guy had emailed me the listing for a 1,400 sq. ft. guesthouse on 20 acres, in the beautiful Woodstock Ranch development, listed at a mere $895, I sighed and told him to stop torturing me.

Two months later, we were driving up the long, steep drive of the property appropriately named "Isla del Cielo." Guy had already seen it by then, though when grilled about the details—does it have heating, and how many rooms, etc.—he was a little fuzzy.

On the day we went up together, it was raining and very cold, the low clouds obscuring most of the property from view. It didn't matter: I was overjoyed. It was a house, a real house…a really funky house, but it was more than we currently had.

When I discovered a guest bedroom and bathroom upstairs, that cinched the deal for me. I was delighted we could have houseguests and they wouldn't have to descend the rickety spiral staircase in the middle of the night to use the bathroom. I instantly fell in love with the place and saw exactly what had to be done to make it right.

Ted held up his end of the bargain and we entered into a long, nerve-wracking escrow. I had long ago learned never to invest hope in a purchase until escrow closed. But I wanted this place more than I had ever wanted anything.

Unfortunately, this property was not only in foreclosure, it also had a tax lien on it that encumbered two properties. The big trick was to get the IRS to lift the lien on the Santa Ynez property and let us close. The escrow was a 49 day nail-biter fraught with obstacles, that finally ended in our favor on April 30th.

From that moment on, our life would take on a whole new dimension, one that was exciting, challenging, and as comforting as it was taxing. It would be the beginning of our nine-year love affair with our enchanting "island in the sky."

The day we closed escrow on our parcel in Woodstock Ranch, I started shopping. Out of fear of jinxing the deal, we hadn't so much as looked at paint colors. But on April 30th, as soon as I got the call, it was time to whip out the credit card. Shortly after the close, we met at the house with our contractor and his foreman and went through room by room, assessing all the changes that needed to be made.

The house was basically square with a long, narrow second floor. It was shaped like a classic barn with high windows running along both sides of the second story, and an exterior staircase leading up to the second bedroom.

The master bedroom, though 20'×16', was as dark as a cave. There were double French doors opening out to the parking area, and a hitching post in front of it. There was no way to get any fresh air into that room unless you opened the French doors. We had them replaced with a 10 ft. window with side casements.

We replaced a long, skinny window with a French door and a screened side light that allowed a cross breeze. We painted the bedroom yellow and our cave became a bright, spacious refuge overlooking the peaks and valleys of Woodstock Ranch and the Santa Ynez Valley beyond.

We painted the entire house—inside and out, walls and cabinetry. We chose different colors for each room, which completely transformed the place. The dark oak cabinet doors in the kitchen became vibrant red, and the ones in the master bath dark blue, to pick up the blue in the Mexican tiles. When we were finished, our little red barn was utterly charming.

While the contractors were diligently working their magic, I was shopping like a professional. As this was our second home, we need everything, including art. It seemed like I shopped non-stop; every day I came home from work with my Jeep loaded down with loot. But even though my credit card was smoking, I was still working full-time and assisting Leah because of the flood of new business.

In the midst of the frenzy, I would occasionally have to make the 45 minute drive over the pass to give instructions or approvals on the work underway. In spite of everything going on, the carpenters, plumbers, electricians, tile setters and painters finished their jobs in less than 60 days. On July 3rd, two months after we closed escrow, we moved in. We were on cloud nine.

We were so in love with our beautiful weekend hideaway, we didn't mind all the hard work that came with it. Even though we were moved in, there was still a lot to be done.

The landscaping—what little was actually planned—had gone completely wild. We had the overgrown area stripped and made countless trips to the local nurseries. We drove around the property in the Kawasaki Mule, gathering rocks to border our flower and cactus beds.

We converted the chicken coop to a vegetable garden. We planted two rows of fruit trees on the slope leading away from the house, which we could see from the north-facing windows, and nine sweet gum trees along the border down by the front of the property to hide the falling down tack room and the hay barn, which our friend Dee christened "the whore house and the jail."

Eventually, everything was as we had envisioned, and every time the front gates swung open and we headed up the driveway, thoughts of work vanished as the thrill of deep satisfaction took its place.

For the first nine months, we'd spent every weekend grooming our new treasure, arriving Friday late afternoon and leaving on Sunday after all the chores were done. In the beginning, we had to travel in separate vehicles because Guy would trailer his two mules, Seamus and Juanita. He finally got wise and hired someone to feed so he could leave them up there. He would ride on the weekends, saddling them on our property and connecting from our front gate to the miles of trails in the association.

I would spend a couple hours every day just digging Russian thistles and pepper tree saplings off the hillsides leading away from the house. Somehow, I'd squeeze in a five-mile walk and an hour or so of writing.

It was hardly what you'd call relaxing, but Woodstock was a labor of love. At the end of the day, depending on the time of year, we'd sip our cocktails out on the deck, watching the sunset, or lounge in front of the large stone fireplace, luxuriating in our amazing good fortune. Either way, it was the realization of a dream for both of us, one I never knew I had.

LUCKY AT LOVE

In September of 2002, Leah got married. It was an event I had looked forward to with equal parts happiness and dread. Because we discovered Leah could run circles around her predecessor, we hadn't hired anyone to fill her former position of assistant processor.

But as the wedding neared and we continued to be swamped with new business, I had become her de facto assistant. Had we known how long the boom was going to last, we probably would've hired someone.

But since that wasn't the case, Leah groomed me to take over the loan processing while she was on her honeymoon. We had become an efficient duo, working in tandem seamlessly. But as her workload increased, so did mine. And though she was confident I could manage while she was away for seven business days, I knew it would be a push to do her job solo, let alone mine.

In the meantime, there was a wedding to look forward to. To her credit, Leah handled all the preparations and her job without becoming a Bridezilla. She did get a little panicky when she couldn't line up anyone to marry her and Zach. Her last lead told her he'd do it if she could postpone the wedding for three months so he'd have time to recover from open-heart surgery.

It was then I recalled that our good friend Gail had gotten a provisional license to officiate at a wedding. We called her, and being the good sport that she is, she agreed to marry Zach and Leah.

The wedding was held outdoors, in a park overlooking the harbor and the Channel Islands. Gail, a naturally wild and spontaneous person, managed an entertaining yet respectful service. The congregation was a mix of young bloods and family, the most colorful being from the bride's father's side.

I had met one of Leah's aunts and two of her cousins at the bridal shower, so I wasn't expecting prim and proper. But as fun and unconventional as that classy trio was, having met them did nothing to prepare me for meeting Uncle Stuey.

As soon as he appeared, all eyes left the bride—who looked even more gorgeous than usual—to stare at this tall, rugged specter. He was decked out in everything ostrich, including his buckaroo hat, and sported a burst of long, frizzy red-grey hair and matching beard. Mirrored aviator sunglasses obscured his eyes.

As soon as Leah saw him, she went flying across the crowd and flung arms and legs around him tightly. We all waited expectantly during this emotional embrace, which required touching up the bride's makeup afterwards. Who was this person? An unlikely babe-magnet, he was quickly surrounded by women, including his sisters and nieces. So this was Uncle Stuey, I thought, as I tried to remember what little I'd been told about him.

What Uncle Stuey lacked in beauty, he made up in charisma. He captivated his flock of female admirers with his Cheshire Cat grin and occasional *bon mots*, including his declaration that some people should never get married, to which he raised his hand. Then he shocked us all by admitting he'd been married and divorced seven times—seven or eight, he couldn't remember which.

Now, his looks, his age (64), and his abysmal track record with women should have made Uncle Stuey highly undesirable among the female guests. Yet, the opposite was true. His unique magnetism appealed to men and women alike. The mother of the groom was so taken with him, she offered to be wife number eight, or nine, while her husband was standing by her side.

Leah had Guy, Gail and me sitting at a table with her father's side of the family. I had Uncle Jerry on my left, Guy on my right and Uncle Stuey on his right. Without any preamble, Stuey informed Guy he was next line if Guy ever got tired of me. I suppose it was a compliment of sorts.

He did have trouble tearing his attention away from me, owing to his partiality to redheads. When he tried to recount which wives had flaming locks, his kin were quick to supply a rundown of his impressive string of nuptials.

Hard as it was to imagine, ol' Stuey had a knack for attracting beautiful, talented women. Judging by his siblings, who were still very striking in their mid-seventies, Stuey must've been at one time quite the looker himself.

But even giving him credit for once having rakish good looks, I still had trouble understanding what made women lose their self-control around him, to the point of saying "I do" despite the long line of former Mrs. Stueys. And why would a man hanker to tie the knot again after so many failed marriages? I was so puzzled by this conundrum, I couldn't get it out of my mind.

While Guy and I walked to our car, I knew I had to find the answers to those questions. As we drove to the office to get a jump on the extra work on my plate, I knew my next book would be about unraveling the secrets of a man addicted to romance, serial marriage, or whatever such a phenomenon is called.

My head was whirring with the prospect, as scenes of a Stuey-type revealed the impulses behind his unquenchable cravings, and what it was about this roguish, borderline clown that women found so irresistible.

I would have to wait eight months before I could begin to find out, as I was only halfway through *Less Than Perfect*. But by the time I finished book number two, I had the whole concept for the new book figured out, and had found the ideal device for cracking open the head of that implausible Casanova to see how it worked.

As with *The Road to Manchac*, it was important for me to relocate my subject and change all the aspects of his life that I was aware of. Uncle Stuey lived in Colorado, where he was involved in ostrich breeding and construction. I made Jake Sorenson a wily mule breeder and trainer who lived in rural Oregon.

I then toyed with different approaches for coaxing the motivation and telling characteristics from my subject. I first saw free-flowing, confession-style dialog as he roved from one location to the next, speaking with bartenders, coffee shop waitresses, or just to the audience at large.

Then I decided I wanted a more controlled environment, such as an interview with a journalist. At some point before I started, I decided the journalist should be a woman. And so, *Lucky at Love* would be told from the point of view of Allison Tyler-Wilcox, a serious journalist, who meets a man at a wedding who had been married and divorced seven times...

Once I started *Lucky*, the characters practically invented themselves. Allison, the protagonist, works for *Savoir Faire Magazine*, and possesses a talent for taking on hard-hitting topics. She becomes fascinated by Jake's numerous nuptials, and convinces her editor there's a story behind what makes some people so attracted to the idea of marriage, despite their terrible track records.

Allison travels to Jake's 1,500 acre Buckin' J Ranch, only to find that she is out-smarted by the wily Jake from the moment she begins the interview process. Their debates become spirited as Jake challenges Allison's beliefs regarding marriage, divorce, life and love.

But Allison can't help but feel drawn in by the man and all his trappings. During her three-day stay, she becomes even more intrigued by the roguish mule breeder and finds it difficult to put him out of her mind.

Leah was unaware that I was writing a book based on meeting her uncle—or that I wrote novels, for that matter—until I broke the news to her when I finished *Lucky*. As shocked as she was on both counts, I was even more shocked to learn that since her wedding, Uncle Stuey had gotten married *again* and had moved from Colorado to Oregon, where he was breeding dogs. Life will always be stranger than fiction.

THE NOT-SO-SIMPLE LIFE

By April 2003, the triangular path of Summerland-Office-Woodstock was wearing me out. The euphoria that came from buying and rehabbing Woodstock had buoyed me above the pain for a time, but then it began to wane. All the coming, going and working till I dropped had caught up with me.

During this time, I had developed another problem. I woke up one night with a crushing feeling in my esophagus, as though something as big as a fist were jammed in there. I couldn't swallow and the pain was intense. I tried taking deep breaths, but it didn't help. Finally, after sitting on the edge of the bed for a few minutes, becoming panicky, I came up with a brilliant idea for relaxing the muscles in my throat.

I went downstairs to the liquor cabinet and poured myself a shot of Jack Daniels. Big mistake. The tiniest sip set off burning pain that almost incapacitated me. Plus, the gyrating in my muscles prevented the booze from going down. I ran to the sink and spit it out. Now I had a fiery fist in my throat. It took several hours for the spasms and pain to pass.

After the second bout with this strange affliction, I went to see Dr. J. When I described the symptoms, he told me I had "functional dyspepsia," and explained that the muscles in the esophagus normally move downward, carrying food and drink to the stomach. The episodes I had experienced were due to the muscles moving the opposite direction, causing painful contractions.

Because these attacks were so alarming, Dr. J prescribed a sublingual tablet I could take at the onset. Since it was impossible to swallow during these bouts, the tablet would dissolve under my tongue, and the mild muscle relaxer would calm the spasms and make it possible to swallow again. From then on, I made sure I had some of these pills with me at all times.

Meanwhile, my other odd symptoms were intensifying. It occurred to me one Sunday as I took my walk—before I had to start cleaning and breaking down the house—that our lifestyle had become too much for me to cope with. I felt that if I kept it up much longer, I'd drop dead.

We still didn't know what, if anything, was wrong with me, but I knew something had to give. Leaving the office on Friday to go back to Summerland to pack up the cat, the food, and the computers, then driving back to Santa Barbara to get Guy, then driving up to the ranch, then repeating the whole thing in reverse on Monday morning had to stop. I saw a solution, a way to cut one leg out of our weekly triangle, and I put it to Guy on the drive home.

For two months we had been showing the back half of our office condo to prospective tenants, as the previous one had suddenly decamped. I told Guy now was the time to act on our desire to turn the back into a crash pad that would cut Summerland out of the loop.

The idea of converting half our space for that purpose was something we had toyed with for years, but now it made sense. Guy agreed with my plan, shockingly, and we got on it right away.

We had roughly 800 sq. ft., just exactly enough to make it all happen. In came the demolition crew, followed by the same gang who'd transformed Woodstock. Two months later, we had a swanky downtown crash pad, with the added benefit of having our business on the other side of the door. As our friend Ted pointed out, we now had a three-inch commute.

Because this was such a novel living situation for us, we looked at it as an experiment we could abandon at any time. But odd as it was being in a beautiful cocoon behind our office, we took to the lifestyle right away. The cat, on the other hand, had a more difficult time adjusting. He had finally become comfortable with the concept of being dragged up to Woodstock and back every week, and this new curve took him a while to accept.

For us, being able to get up from our desks at the end of an action-packed day and walk to any one of the dozens of restaurants in a four block radius, was reminiscent of living in the French Quarter. In slower times, I would email Guy movie choices and times, and we'd cut out early and walk two or three blocks to catch an early film.

And that's the way we would spend Monday through Wednesday nights. Thursday afternoons, we'd head up to the ranch, to a lifestyle that was completely opposite to our downtown gig.

Our new situation suited us so well, we all but forgot about our Summerland house. We moved into the apartment—after another shopping spree—in August of 2003, and we didn't go back to Summerland together until January, and only then to make sure there hadn't been any damage after a heavy storm.

Finally, after settling into a comfortable groove, we realized we should lease Summerland out as a vacation rental. We had walked away from it, taking only our clothes and personal items. Everything else was just as we had left it, including the pantry and the liquor cabinet. It just didn't make sense to leave the place vacant and unused. Renting it out was the only sensible thing to do.

Once we got our heads around the concept, I made several trips to the house to clear out closets and drawers—seventeen years of accumulated *stuff*, things crammed out of sight and out of mind.

It took hours of agonizing purging to make the place suitable for guests. Guy put together a website and joined rental listing services like VRBO. I was lucky enough to find a cleaning service that specialized in vacation rentals and knew what it took to clean up after tenants and prepare for the next.

In no time, we had our first month-long booking. After that, the calendar filled up quickly, and we discovered we had a very nice additional revenue stream. But it didn't take us long to figure out that with the extra income came extra jobs: Guy was the booking agent, and I was the one who made everything right after the cleaning crew did their thing. I can't even calculate how many hours this new enterprise took out of Guy's life. I didn't spend as much time on it, but it was all physical.

In addition to buying paper products and sundries in bulk for the office, the apartment and Woodstock, I now did the same for Summerland. I would replace soap, detergent, toilet paper, etc. after every departure and spend an hour or two putting everything back where it belonged. I scrubbed spots off walls and carpets and set out fresh flowers. I also spent a good deal of time buying new towels—bath and pool.

Somewhere along the way, I realized my brilliant idea of simplifying my life had backfired. But there was nothing to be done about that now; the house—with its three bedrooms, swimming pool, ocean/island/mountain views—was booking a year in advance. We were now slaves to our new business, spread even thinner than we were before.

But we couldn't complain too much. Renting Summerland was found money. And as the bookings kept on coming, it was too much money to walk away from. Besides, this had been a self-inflicted hardship. There was only one way to increase our madness, and Guy found it.

In April of 2004, after visiting Josiah, Guy's son, and his fiancée, Justine, at their home in Palm Springs, Guy got a wild hair, went online and found a charming, 4 bed/4 bath 1946 Spanish hacienda for sale. He showed me the photo tour, excited about the vacation rental potential. I oohed and ahhed appropriately, not taking his interest seriously.

Next thing I knew, Guy announced he was going to make an offer, as he dashed to the fax machine. I sputtered out a couple questions—*what could it rent for per night, and at what occupancy rate would it cash flow*—in hopes of starting a sensible dialog. It was too late. Guy cavalierly waved my concerns away, sending the fax that would promptly be accepted. I had no idea he was capable of such a rash act.

I like to think of this episode as Guy's midlife crisis. How he got caught up in the Palm Springs buying frenzy, I'll never understand. Prior to our visit, we hadn't been to Palm Springs in fourteen years, and neither of us remembered it fondly. But two days after the offer was accepted, we boarded a plane to check out our latest acquisition.

The house was charming, there was no doubt about it. I liked it, in spite of myself. I don't know, maybe the heat did something to our brains. All I know is that my usual radar and skepticism must've been on the fritz during our two-hour inspection. I guess the fountains and palm trees and the pool area and the separate casita obscured more practical issues that we were forced to deal with after escrow closed.

There was another offer on the table, and in that highly charged market that made the place even more appealing to Guy. The question of *why are we doing this?* got lost in the heat waves emanating from the scorched earth. After a slam-dunk escrow, we were the proud owners of another vacation rental. Oh joy.

Naturally, I had very real reservations about properly maintaining the place from such a distance. I knew how much effort it took on a weekly basis to keep a vacation rental up. No problem. The management company would take care of everything.

If I could've seen into the future and gotten a glimpse of the ongoing agony that dealing with an older home and an overloaded management company would cause Guy, I would've done anything to change his mind. For five long, aggravating years, Guy would be at the mercy of his hasty decision. I have never seen him more outraged and furious than he was with issues at Casa Bonita.

But that was all in the future. In the meantime, we had a four bedroom house to furnish. I went on a shopping mission like I never hope to repeat. Everything our Summerland house had to offer had to be replicated, Spanish style.

I don't know how I managed it, but barely five weeks after the close, I had pulled together an entire house of furniture, including dozens of framed prints, mirrors, Mexican pottery, bed and bath linens, and absolutely every plate, glass, pot, pan and utensil one could possibly need. Not to mention the televisions, telephones, clock radios and hairdryers for each bedroom.

It took an entire week, seven days of non-stop work to get the furniture moved in and everything put in its place. I had never worked so hard in my life. But when we were finished, the house was a thing of beauty. After causing me so much anxiety and acrimony, Casa Bonita became a treasure I hated to leave in the hands of others.

From that moment on, the house would never be the same. When we closed the gates behind us and turned it over for renting, the honeymoon was over. All the money and attention to decorating would never be treated the way it should've been. It was a Palm Springs vacation rental, and those houses probably take more abuse than any.

The one good thing about owning that place was being able to use it when Josiah and Justine got married in September. And on those few occasions when we spent time in the house, we really enjoyed it. If only the story had ended there.

Under the Weather

If I thought I could give my mystery illness the slip by ignoring it and working myself to the bone, I was wrong. At no time did my vast array of symptoms let up; through all the extracurricular actives, from the purchase of Woodstock onward, I continued to deteriorate. Big surprise. What did I expect?

It's easy for me to see the foolishness of my lifestyle from my current prospective. But I have to remind myself that according to most of the doctors I'd seen, there was really nothing wrong with me. The visit to the endocrinologist had such a demoralizing effect, the thought of seeking out another medical opinion made me feel worse than I already did.

But my episodes of extreme pain and decreased coordination were more troubling to Guy than they were to me. He would beg, cajole, and threaten to drag me to the nearest "specialist." We went round and round on the issue of my degrading health, until finally I'd give in and *"go see somebody."*

I had seen three rheumatologists and one neurologist—plus other doctors—to no avail. As I had felt from the very beginning that my problems seemed to stem from a neurological disorder, I made an appointment with another neurologist, Dr. M.

Dr. M saw how desperate I was to find answers and a treatment, and after acing another battery of tests, he was still willing to stick it out with me until we found some way of relieving my pain.

His gut feeling was I had fibromyalgia, despite the fact that none of 18 trigger points used to diagnose the condition caused me any special discomfort. I explained how my symptoms were really not in line with fibromyalgia symptoms and that the medications I'd been given in the past did nothing to help the pain.

On my third visit, seeing how emotionally beaten down I was, Dr. M offered to try me on a variety of meds that work well for fibromyalgia, even though he didn't normally treat patients with that disorder.

Since he was willing and compassionate, I gave it a chance, trying five different drugs with no success, only an unsettling assortment of side effects, which he had warned me about. I thought some of the risks didn't sound too troubling, until I started experiencing them. We were both disappointed when one drug after the other failed to relieve the pain. When I got down to the fifth and final drug and started having horrific hallucinations, I tossed it out and gave up—again.

In 2004, right after Josiah and Justine got married, my sainted mother-in-law was diagnosed with renal cancer. It was a terrible shock, even with all her medical problems. She was doing so well at the wedding just two weeks prior to her hospitalization. She had looked better than ever and had much more energy. I think the prospect of her grandson getting married had kept her spirits high, in spite what was going on in her body.

As she was getting on in her years, and because Guy and his mother were so close, we planned a trip to see her in February of that year. Right before the trip I got very sick. I spent all day Sunday shivering by the roaring fire, mummified in Uggs, parka, scarf and gloves. Nothing could make me warm, not even the fever.

As Guy packed up the cat and the food to go back to the office Monday morning, I drove into Santa Ynez to see a doctor friend of ours. I was convinced I had strep throat and a kidney infection, because the pain in my back was so intense. Dr. Shannon ran the two tests right in his office, and both came back negative. He gave me a Z-pak in case the more conclusive strep test came back positive.

With all the strength I could muster, I drove back up to the ranch. I couldn't go back to the office because Leah's four-month-old baby girl came to the office with her every day. And though Sydney had her own private office up front across from her mother, I didn't want to risk giving her any part of what I had. As luck would have it, our first tenants had just moved into Summerland, so that wasn't an option.

So, I cranked up the heat, piled all the blankets I could find onto the bed, put on several layers of clothes *and* my parka *and* my Uggs, crawled under the covers and shook violently. I was wracked with body aches, which was customary for me, but these were much worse. I was used to unexplained chills, but they were nothing like these. I knew this was no ordinary bad day.

The night brought with it a horrific storm. Dr. Shannon's wife, Jeanne, was worried about me being all alone at the ranch and wanted to come rescue me, but it was really too treacherous to be out. Rain beat so hard against the west side of the house, it began to seep in over and under the door to our bedroom, something it had never done before or since. I dammed it up the best I could and spent the rest of the night moaning and groaning and being otherwise pathetic.

Being a good friend and a good doctor, Jeff Shannon called in the morning to check on me. As soon as I answered the phone, he knew I had pneumonia. The deep, soggy cough I'd developed overnight gave me away.

He was glad he'd given me the antibiotics when I was there, because there was no way I could've ventured out for any reason; the storm was raging and no letup was in sight. He offered to pay me a visit, bring me anything I needed, but I declined. For all I knew, our driveway had become a steep river of mud. I was stuck there, all alone, and that was that.

Every now and then, hunger forced me out of bed in search of something to eat. I was really too weak to manage much and Guy had taken most of the food back to the apartment. Plus, even with the heater blasting, my shivering drove me back under the covers, though it didn't stop the shaking.

Desperate for warmth, I tried defrosting myself in the bath a couple of times, but as soon as I dried off I was freezing again. I can truly say this was one of the most agonizing and pitiful experiences I ever had.

Somehow, three days passed, and on Thursday afternoon Guy and the kitty came back up to the ranch. I was feeling strong enough by then to put fresh clothes on and eat some dinner. When my jeans nearly fell off me, I got on the scale and discovered I had literally shaken off 10 pounds in four days. The oversize butt that had followed me around since high school was gone. Completely gone. I was skin and bones. It would take me a year of voracious eating to get back to normal.

Looking back now, I find it amazing I survived pneumonia on top of the Lyme I didn't even know I had, without hospitalization or even someone to check on me, feed me cough medicine or pat me on the hand.

Now it was only five days until we were to fly to New Orleans. I felt a little better every day, but in hindsight, I probably shouldn't have gone. Once we got there, I could tell it was too soon to be traveling. I felt like a monster visiting Elena at the Maison Hopitaliere in the French Quarter, where she lived with dozens of other elderly folks. But Elena was in high spirits, having been chosen as the Mardi Gras Queen of the Maison. It was great to see her so happy.

Knowing now that she had less than a year to live, I'm glad I made the trip. We had a wonderful time with her in September at the wedding, and I went to see her again after her diagnosis, before she went to hospice. In December, just three months after Josiah and Justine's wedding, she passed away.

I was very blessed to have had a mother-in-law who was so loving. She was very social, loved meeting new people, and she lit up whenever her loved ones were around her.

She and I had a special bond; at times she felt more like a friend than a mother-in-law. We could become incredibly goofy together when playing Trivial Pursuit and the other games we got into after the big Sunday feasts, when she would cook her famous bresola and lasagna. She never once found fault with me. Everything I did was "tremendous." That's the way she was with everyone in her family. Elena was love itself.

Losing her hit me much harder than I was prepared for. For years, I had worried how Guy would react when she died. I had been worrying about the wrong person. On the trips back to visit her before her death, Guy came to grips with her imminent passing. This was a huge relief for me, but being so focused on how he would handle it, I didn't realize I was the one who'd fall apart.

For her burial service, Elena had chosen a close friend to read a letter she had written long before her final illness. When I heard my name being read along with the names of her four children, I felt my heart crack in half. The simple act of including me as one of her own was more proof of her love than I ever expected to find. To say I was devastated would be an understatement.

During Elena's final illness, I was working on my fourth book, *Alligators in the Trees,* which I think she would've really enjoyed, especially having lived in New York. She had read the previous three books, and even though she appeared in *The Road to Manchac,* her favorite was *Lucky at Love.* She wanted to meet Jake, or rather, marry him. This would become a common response from women who would eventually read the book. Even men have told me Jake is someone they'd like to know.

While working on *Lucky,* a new book started to come together in my head. Until it was finished, I called it simply Book 4. The eventual title came from a line in a song written toward the end by Priscilla, one of the three principle characters.

As was the case with the three previous books, the story revolved around a character invented to support the protagonist. But as it developed, it became Priscilla's story, subtly unseating Tobias as the lead, though all three main characters have their own plot lines and entourages that orbit around them.

The seed for this book came from a renewed appreciation of a rock band that had been part of my life's soundtrack in my teen years, and on into my 20's and 30's. The band, consisting of two main partners, reunited briefly to go on tour after a decades-long split. Since Guy and I were both big fans, we bought tickets when the band came to the Santa Barbara County Bowl.

Excited about seeing a group that neither of us had seen live, we spent the intervening weeks reacquainting ourselves with their unique style. It was during this period of renewed appreciation for their sublime lyrics and complex melodies that I started to ponder what the lead singer was like in his personal life. What provoked him to write such clever, enigmatic lyrics? What were his demons and his passions? Where did his exceptional talent stem from?

Musing about the lead singer/songwriter's muses caused me to imagine what might go on inside the head of such a gifted musician. Tobias Jordan was the fruit my imagination bore: a '90s rock legend with a combustible marriage and a penchant for young models, who is urged into a comeback by his wife and his former partner, primarily for the money it would generate.

I had my main character; now I needed the supporting cast.

Priscilla Vanderpool was drafted after an encounter with a waitress at Pea Soup Anderson's in Buellton. For some reason I decided a coffee shop waitress would be a good foil for the surly, paparazzi-phobic rocker. But as I worked out her character, I decided the story needed a third wheel, someone the other two could spin off of. But I couldn't quite picture who the third person should be.

One night while we were out to dinner in Santa Barbara, a client of Guy's came over to our table to say hello. In his capacity as architect, he had created artistically stunning homes, drawing mostly from his love of Italy. His demeanor vacillated between distracted and aloof, to dreamily absorbed in the moment.

As the conversation went along, it hit me I'd found my missing component. A passionately artistic architect with his head in the clouds would fill the void perfectly. And so, Philip Glessner, once renowned for his innovative designs, and now disgraced by the collapse of his signature building, became the third element in what would turn into a highly unusual triangle.

Frank's Coffee Shop becomes a safe haven for Philip as he eludes a posse of blood-thirsty reporters. Tobias is drawn to the anonymity of the non-descript eatery. What keeps both of them coming back is Priscilla—an improbable paragon of virtue to the shell-shocked Philip, and an unwitting muse to the cynical and gifted Tobias.

Now that I had the premise and the characters sorted out, I realized I had put myself in the position of having to write song lyrics from two different perspectives. What did I know about songwriting? Nothing. It was a challenge, but I took my cues from Priscilla and Tobias, tapping into what was going on in their respective subconscious minds by observing their actions.

New Beginnings

From this vantage point, 2005 is mostly a blur. Life consisted of work, weekly migrations from the apartment/office to Woodstock and back, dealing with the vacation rentals, writing (an hour here, an hour there) and all the trivialities of daily life. Plus pain—lots of pain.

A typical weekday consisted of working out (often in the middle of the night when I couldn't sleep) plugging away at my computer until noon, running to the store for groceries, making lunch.

After cleaning up, I'd collapse in the back for an hour, an interlude too marred by relentless, savage pains to be considered restful. Then back to my office until Guy was ready to call it a day. We'd change clothes, take a walk and go to dinner. I was fine with everything about our unconventional lifestyle, but the pain I could've done without.

In October of that year, Guy's daughter, Emma, and her fiancé, Dave got married. They had been together for five years and made a great couple. They had moved to New York City in January of 2002, which was where the wedding was held.

Unfortunately, I was having a hard time physically and wasn't able to help setting up the venue. I did show up, late, and tried to give moral support. It was one of those occasions where I really felt like I had failed to do what was needed of me. But I did manage to rally in time for the ceremony the next evening, and took part in the festivities afterwards with everyone else.

2005 also brought the birth of a new business venture, which is nice way of saying I somehow talked Guy into letting me self-publish. I had not put much effort in to finding an agent to represent me; in fact, I hadn't even paused long enough after the second book to even draft a query. I had made lackluster attempts after the first book and *Lucky*, but I hadn't even thought of seeking representation for *Alligators*.

I think it was cowardice that made me eschew the traditional road to publishing in favor of leaping into something I knew nothing about. But I did a good enough sales job on Guy, convincing him that taking my books directly to readers was good business sense.

Whether he agreed with my logic or not, he okayed the idea and the expenditures, putting his money on my writing ability and not on my expertise in self-publishing. But lack of knowledge didn't worry me. I'd bought a book. I would know exactly what to do.

I can't recall the name of the book now, but it was full of helpful information. I read it and tried to follow the authors' advice to the letter. There was so much to consider and it was such a huge undertaking.

Looking back, I'm surprised I was less daunted by the prospect of forming a publishing company than I was by the thought of endless rejection slips. But fear is a funny thing, and I suppose the fear of sending my works out only to have them rewarded with an unceremonious return trip back outweighed the fear of the unknown.

But there was something else behind my desire to self-publish, another fear I didn't share with anyone. I was afraid that if I didn't take this rash step, I'd never live long enough to be published through normal channels.

After writing solely for self-gratification, I finally realized it was important to me that at least one of my books made it into print while I was still around to appreciate the thrill. I never spoke of the true motivating factor because I didn't want to sound morbid or melodramatic. After all, there still wasn't anything officially wrong with me. *I* knew there was something very wrong with me, and I knew I was steadily deteriorating, regardless of what the experts thought.

In any event, I went at this self-publishing concept with an abundance of enthusiasm, starting a company from the ground up. I could've found a basic printing company if I just wanted copies of my book to sell from the back of my car, and then I could've skipped all the hoopla.

But I was bound and determined to give my books a proper chance in the marketplace. This meant forming a publishing company, which was necessary in order for my titles to be listed with Bowker, which is required by book distributors.

So, we made it official, creating Woodstock Press as a subsidiary of our parent corporation. I got my business license, my resale license, created a logo so we could have letterhead printed. We setup a website—a rather basic one—but it performed its main function, which was to sell books.

After researching book manufactures, I ended up going with a full-service printing company, which had a built-in distribution component. It was all systems go, with me, the fearless leader at the helm. Brimming in optimism, I bought ten ISBNs. We were ready for business.

Against popular opinion, I chose to lead this publishing bonanza with *Lucky at Love* instead of *Alligators in the Trees*, which Guy and Leah believed to be the stronger of the two books, but my instincts told me that *Lucky's* storyline would appeal to a larger audience.

With that settled—by me, the head honcho—we began the task of putting the book together. The company I hired, Bookbastards—obviously not the real name, but one I think is more fitting—gave me bids for copy editing, composing text (the laying out of each page), cover design, etc.

The costs for editing and composing text were huge, but I was persuaded that their editing department was extremely professional, with hundreds of titles to their credit. I was also made more amenable to the thought of forking over so much dough by the veiled threat that their company would not be liable for any errors made by outside editing, whereas they would stand behind their work and make any corrections, if need be.

I acquiesced, being the superstitious chicken that I am. But I couldn't swallow the thought of spending nearly five grand on composing text, something that we (Leah) could do with software that cost less than $300.

After making that compromise and saving our company thousands—*whew!*—I went ahead and took them up on their cover design proposal. Fortunately, the guy handling the project was very easy to deal with.

I had an idea in mind, something relatively simple that I was able to describe to the artist. I saw the title in a loose script, with a horseshoe for the *u* in *Lucky*, and the *e* in *Love* falling off the end, two hints which conveyed equines were part of the story and that maybe someone wasn't really as lucky at love as he'd like to think.

Along the bottom of the cover is the subtitle: *Some guys just never give up...*, referencing Jake's uncommon fortitude in the matrimony department. Because *Lucky at Love* sounds like the title of a romance novel, I wanted to make sure the cover said otherwise.

For the background, I kept coming back to a scene from the book where Allison and Jake are sitting on a bench outside one of Jake's barns, with an unsettling number of stars above their heads. I had the artist create an hombre sky, the deep blue fading above a silhouette of barns, outbuildings and trees. White stars dot the background. It was effective, and the color palette also contradicted the notion that this was strictly a woman's book.

As I didn't know I should've hired a publicist by this time to generate favorable reviews from established authors, I went with the classic hardcover approach of having my photo on the back. This of course meant I needed to hire a photographer, one who would hopefully capture a photo of me I could live with forever. Fortunately, I found one.

As I discussed possible locations for the background with Amy Lundstrom, she asked about the cover design. When I broke it down for her, she said it would be nice if we could find a rural setting for the shoot. Not a problem, I told her—I had just the place, only a short drive over the pass. She was game, and in early December of '05, we met up at Woodstock on a cool and windy afternoon.

Amy was inspired by the ranch; with intermittent wardrobe changes, we hoofed all over the property, finding infinite backdrops and great natural lighting. The end result of our two-hour romp over hill and dale was a staggering collection of 498 photos. My stomach lurched when I opened the file and realized what I had gotten myself into. I immediately closed out and went to the back to lie down.

Guy, being more curious and less skeptical, waded through all of the photos. He managed to convince me there were some nice ones in the horde, and eventually I got up the nerve to look for myself. He was right; there were a few I couldn't find fault with. We chose one that seemed to be the most in keeping with the spirit of the book, a shot of me leaning against the white gate that led to the back driveway, with the shadowy valley as a backdrop.

Now for the blurb on the cover flap. By this time, I was starting to see the advantages of going the traditional route, of enticing a publisher enough to take a gamble on my work, make me an offer and then take care of all the details that go into publishing a book, such as writing the blurb.

Since I didn't have that luxury, I put on my advertising hat and tried to sum up the story of Allison and Jake, hopefully making it appealing enough for the average book shopper to become sufficiently intrigued. After an inordinate amount of labor, I eventually ended up with a fairly good description. I ran it past my collaborators and we went with it. That done, we had our cover. Now we were excited.

During this time, the editing department was supposedly hard at work on the text. After weeks of delays and numerous phone calls, they emailed me the edited version with instructions on how to save or delete the changes.

This much-anticipated event quickly turned into a nightmare when I discovered the editor had corrected things that didn't need correcting (like foreign words) and missed things that were obviously wrong and somehow got missed in our umpteen proof readings. There were many distressed calls to the head of the department, and the long and short of it was they'd put their most senior editor on it.

Once we got the final revisions, we just needed the text to be composed as it would be in the final product. Leah, between pulling her hair out and talking to tech support for hours, cracked the secrets of the software and converted the Word doc to the proper fit for a 352 page book.

Leah did a great job, designing the overall look of each page. She came up with flourishes, the correct line for each new chapter to appear, the number of lines per page and the correct number of blank pages, plus the recto, verso, title page, dedication and acknowledgement pages. Off it went to the printer to be put to the test in the galley stage.

With the delays, there was one obligation we were in danger of screwing up. A friend in a neighboring office suggested bringing the book to her reading group. Marti's month was April. Because we had started the process in the fall of the previous year, this didn't seem like it would be an issue.

But since the galleys come first and must be read and approved before the book could even be scheduled for printing, I knew there was no way we were going to make Marti's deadline of mid-March. *Would galleys be okay?* Marti said it would be fine, as long as they arrived in time. No problem, I told her confidently.

The galleys arrived in time, barely. I rushed them next door to Marti before I had a chance to review a copy myself. When I was able to examine this amazing fruit of all our labors, a ragged bolt of panic ripped through my insides: there was a typo.

Horrified, I emailed Marti to alert her of this oversight. She answered me back saying she'd seen it. Had I seen the ones on pages 9 and 13? *There were more?* I read on, sweating bullets every time I came across another error. By this time I felt completely sick. What had the editing department been doing all this time?

Okay, I'm the one who made all those errors to start with, having an increasingly harder time with my brain-hand-eye coordination. But isn't that why you pay for professional editing? Because the printer was back East, I had to wait until the following morning to contact them. I didn't sleep a minute that night.

After floating in a cloud of naiveté, it hit me what a gamble I had taken. I was in over my head. I wasn't equipped to deal with the pitfalls of self-publishing. I hadn't taken into consideration that there were disreputable book printers. I had cavalierly thrown a pile of money at this publishing scheme and there was no turning back now, no matter what the results.

Looking back, I can see how this increased stress played havoc with my illness. It was the beginning of a declining trajectory. From that point on, I no longer had confidence and hope to buoy me through the arduous process I had embarked on. Now I doubted every claim and assurance I had been given by the Bookbastards.

My newfound skepticism didn't come a moment too soon. Even though my rep promised everything would be corrected, I no longer believed her. I was leery of every word she said, and every email to her that went unanswered made me panic more.

I was able to create enough of a stink with the editing department to get immediate action, but correcting the mistakes didn't include reprinting the galleys. Their attitude was, "That's what galleys are for." The flawed galleys would have to be sent out to reviewers, giving me such a feeling of apprehension and failure.

Marti and her friends were gracious enough to read the flawed galleys, and meeting with the group was very rewarding for me. Being part of their reading experience made all I'd been through worthwhile. It was an author's dream scenario: praise for the product of countless hours of isolated writing. That one meeting fired me right up again.

It was suggested to me by the rep who set up our website, Lars Clausen, a writer himself, that I speak to the publicist he used to market his self-published book. I took his advice, only to find out she was leaving for a month-long vacation and would not have sufficient time to meet our publishing date, which was three months away. She would've needed six months, minimum.

Had I known then what I would learn later, I would've changed our publishing date from June to sometime in the fall. I could tell this woman knew her stuff. She had gotten Lars's book reviewed in *Publisher's Weekly*, which is no easy feat, especially for a self-published author. She gave me lots of free advice, which further underscored the need for a publicist.

Guy did some research and found a firm in New York that seemed to have good credentials and a base of well-known, satisfied clients. He filled out the online form, but we didn't hear back from them for two months. The owner claimed there was a problem with their email during this period, but it seems more likely that business had dried up and they were dredging through deleted emails when they came across ours. This is hindsight, of course. At the time, we were relieved she had gotten back to us.

This publicist (for whom I don't have a clever fake name) gave me a rundown on the services she could offer us: for $6,000, her team would put together a publicity package consisting of a press release, queries for interviews and reviews, and a Q&A designed to give information about me and my book to the reading public. She sent us a sample package which I can't say I was overly impressed with, but it didn't include examples of the real enticements, which were possible live and print interviews.

Six-thousand dollars was a lot of cabbage. But our research had led us to conclude that we really needed a publicist, and because our publishing date was fast approaching, we weren't finding any other takers. So, painful as it was, we pulled the trigger and hired her.

The phone appointment to close the deal would be the last time I would speak to her. From that moment on, one of her "associates" would handle our account. I'll never forget her ominous remark after we placed our hopes and our cash in her hands: "Two months really isn't enough time. I'm not sure what we can do, but we'll give it a shot." Not exactly the confidence-building sign I was looking for, but more of an indication of the bad bargain I had just made.

When our "publicity package" arrived, I was dumbfounded by its meager contents. To make matters worse, the so-called Press Release was taken word for word from the blurb I had written for the book cover. Nothing added, nothing taken away.

I had another well-deserved bout of self-doubt, but I knew making an issue out of this wasn't going to do me any good. Besides, at this point I was barely holding it together physically. My many go-rounds with the printing company had left me worse for wear. I just had to play along with the charade for whatever benefit it would generate.

The trainee, or glorified assistant, or whatever she was, who was assigned to our project kept me abreast of all the obscure avenues for possible interviews she was pursuing. She was very excited when she had secured an online interview with a website devoted to romance novels. I cringed.

I do not consider *Lucky at Love* to be a romance novel. In my Q&A I made that perfectly clear. In my mind, a story about a guy who's been married and divorced *seven times* does not a romance novel make. The book is more a philosophical debate on marriage and divorce, with a dash of accidental romance. But since this was the only nibble we'd gotten, I sucked it in and devoted myself to one of the weirdest days I've ever spent.

The "interview" was conducted by employees of this site by posting questions which I would then answer. Their members would also join in and ask questions about the book, me, my inspiration, whatever.

This all sounded fairly straightforward and simple enough. I would pretend for one day I had written a romance novel, despite the lack of steamy love scenes, and Woodstock Press would send a copy of the book to anyone who participated. To help, my "publicist" would facilitate, feeding me questions if there was ever a lag in the conversation.

There I sat at my computer, door shut, trying to make the most of the situation, and wishing for the day to pass. The glitches came early and for most of our allotted time, the responses I tried to post weren't received due to a service outage with the webhost. Naturally. The connection was finally restored just before my session ended. Fine, who cares? I had survived and it was over.

I emailed a list of addresses to Leah so she could send out copies of the book to the participants. When I staggered up to her desk, she could barely suppress a laugh as she informed me that one of the participants lived in Iceland, and the postage for sending the book to her was $27.35, more than the cover price of the hardback.

Sadly, that was the grand finale as far as the publicist went. The assistant would make weekly contact with me to say nothing new had surfaced. I felt completely *had* and completely stupid.

I hadn't listened to my gut feeling when this woman appeared two months later; I wanted to believe she could give the book a proper send-off. I wanted to believe we'd get something for our $6,000 other than an online interview with a romance genre site. But I had to face the fact that I had wasted precious resources and done next to nothing to promote our book. That was a lesson I could've done without, but it was a lesson I would never forget.

THE SHOW MUST GO ON

What I learned about self-publishing is this: it's not glamorous, it's not for the faint-hearted and it's not for the infirm.

There came a point where I felt so horrible, if I could've undone all that I'd done towards self-publishing, I would have. But if I could've undone that, I would've certainly undone getting sick and eliminated all my agonies. But what's behind you can't be changed. All I could do was keep my head down and trudge forward, donning my best face and pretending all was going according to plan.

Somewhere between the galley episode and my brother's wedding reception in late May 2006, I sucked up enough courage to seek out another doctor. I was in dire straits. I could barely walk now. I would get out of bed in the morning and stumble and lurch, as though I had no control over my feet. I almost couldn't stand because of the pain. I had already been to three rheumatologists, but it now seemed that seeing a fourth might be the best approach. I just didn't know what else to do.

I got Dr. N's name through a friend, though her opinion was somewhat mixed: Dr. N may be lacking in bedside manner, but he was a very good doctor. He may not offer sympathy, but he knew how to make his patients well. I was a little daunted by the prospect of seeing a doctor with such a formidable reputation, but the hope of getting to the bottom of my problems spurred me forward.

It was almost impossible for me to not conjure up some image of what meeting with a new doctor was going to be like. After the first three or four, I no longer expected my visits to have a successful outcome. Hope was the reason I went, but skepticism and trepidation would always accompany me to my appointments.

The longer I had to wait between phone call and office visit, the longer my imagination had to create a wide variety of scenarios. The thought of waiting for a verdict from another unknown entity would sometimes make me nervous enough to cancel. Why would it be any different this time?

"You have to go see him," Guy would say. So I would go, despite my misgivings. I suppose seeing a new doctor isn't really any different than going on a blind date, except that the hoped-for outcome is not finding a soul mate but finding a cure.

From the minute I walked into Dr. N's office, I felt an undercurrent of disappointment. The diehard optimist in me could not explain away my suspicion that this was not the office of a medical genius. The receptionist was nice enough, but ditzy—ditzy in a way that made ordinary efficiency improbable. The fact that she was the only personnel in the office was my second hint that Dr. N apparently wasn't in vogue enough to require a normal size staff.

The chatter I overheard from the waiting room informed me that the doctor had enough time on his hands to chat with pharmaceutical reps, something most doctors don't have the luxury or patience for. I was no stranger to long waits, but not usually due to idle chitchat.

As I sat there, I was able to glean characteristics of the man who I had hoped would be canny enough to zero in on the cause of my problems. I got a glimpse of him; I heard the superior, mocking tone in his voice. I knew in my gut this appointment was not going to yield any promising revelations.

As with so many doctors' visits in the past, I could've just walked out of the office and been no worse off for leaving. Getting better under his care wasn't in the cards. I could feel it.

The door opened and the rep kept the banter going as she headed out the door. Dr. N stood there, eyeing his only patient in the waiting room. He crooked his finger and I collected my things and followed him into a small examination room, not much different from than the countless cubicles I been in over the last seven years. But the doctor was definitely different. What luck for me: I had scored an appointment with the Robin Williams of rheumatology.

From the start, he made it known he was in control of the interview process. He would ask questions, then partially listen to the responses, become irreverent when the spirit moved him, amuse himself for my benefit, fasten his attention on me until a new cause for derision presented itself.

Somewhere over the course of the comedy routine, Dr. N performed a physical examination. His demeanor became more serious as he poked and prodded around. After a thorough sizing-up, he confided in me that he suspected ankylosing spondylitis.

I couldn't even get my brain around the name, let alone repeat it. Dr. N wrote it down and told me to look it up on the internet. He then filled out a lab slip for a full blood panel, including a test for the prime suspect. He would see me back in his office in two weeks, and in the meantime, I was to take a six-day course of prednisone.

Two weeks later, I was back in Dr. N's forum. I had taken the prednisone, which had made a noticeable difference. I knew prednisone was not something to be taken for any length of time, being a type of steroid. I also now knew that ankylosing spondylitis was an unlikely diagnosis; though I had severe pain in my spine, I also had many other pains and symptoms that were not hallmarks of the disease.

Dr. N read through my test results as he entered the exam room. He continued to ponder the information for a couple of minutes before voicing his disappointment. My test results were normal. Nearly perfect, in fact.

Whatever small hope I had of finally getting a concrete diagnosis withered. The only abnormality in my blood work was an elevated ANA level. This was news: nothing on any of my previous tests had been abnormal. I was always the picture of health, on paper.

Maybe this was a hopeful sign. Maybe now the veil was beginning to drop. Dr. N wasn't interested in the high ANA level; his mind had fastened onto ankylosing spondylitis and wasn't ready to let it go.

"I can't prove it," Dr. N said solemnly, "but I truly believe you have ankylosing spondylitis."

"Is it something that can be treated?" I asked cautiously. If this was the only flavor on offer, I figured I should at least consider it. What else did I have to go on?

"There are two drugs that work very well on this disease—Embrel and Humira. They cost about $2,000 a month. I would like you to take either of them for at least two months to see if they help." *$4,000 to see if they work?* I couldn't believe my ears.

What about the high ANA? Wasn't that a more solid clue to follow? I didn't have ankylosing spondylitis, and I sure the hell wasn't going to spend four grand to prove him wrong. I left Dr. N's office feeling defeated by the randomness of the universe and the unlikelihood of ever knowing what was really wrong with me.

I didn't start reading for pleasure until I was 19. But once I started, I became a book junkie, sometimes having five different books going at one time. I had a lot of lost time to make up for, and there was so much out there to immerse myself in. I went from being almost proud of my illiteracy to being ashamed of my obliviousness. I joined book clubs and always ordered several books at a time, for fear of running out of something to read.

Once I moved to Santa Barbara, I had several wonderful bookstores to haunt. It was such a treat to browse while trying to broaden my horizons, usually at the bargain tables. Books were my escape, the way they are for many people.

But for all my love of the written word, becoming a writer never entered my mind. I was in awe of writers, marveling at their ability to spin tales, expand minds and entertain the reader with their own visions of the world, capturing nebulous thoughts and mounting them on pages for all to see. Never did I imagine that I would ever attempt such a thing.

I have two distinct memories of being stupefied by the process of writing. The first was when I saw *Out of Africa*. There is a scene where the Baroness von Blixen is challenged by her two male guests to finish a tale from a one-sentence cue. She does so, with such fluidity, even if it never happened in real life, it was a searing image that made me believe true writing talent was a God-given gift only a small number of exceptional beings ever possessed. I would think about that scene and I would be immediately awed.

I found a second reinforcement of this theory in the book *Crossing to Safety* by Walter Stegner. In the story, the protagonist is a university professor who writes novels in his spare time, cramming an hour of writing in before work, during lunch, at night before bed. The result of his efforts is so good, he is published by the first firm to receive the manuscript.

Now, writing this, I realize at least one of these recollections is of a fictional account, and therefore cannot be held up as examples of brilliance, except that both stem from the imagination of two esteemed authors. That ability to imagine and to grapple to the page a story of continuity and interest, of a believable tale told with simplicity and insight was something I could never do in a million lifetimes.

Yet, I somehow forgot this when wracking my brain for a creative outlet I could pursue from bed, if it came to that. Once I had forgotten I was lacking the fundamental ability, I discovered I was capable of making up characters out of thin air, giving them a series of dilemmas and letting them run wild.

But when the driver from the Yellow Trucking Company brought in the first cases of *Lucky at Love* hardcovers, I felt as though there had been some sort of mix-up in my destiny. How was it that I was holding a book with *my* name on it, *my* words and characters inside? Did I deserve this honor, even if I had bestowed it on myself?

That's what I would find out once readers got hold of them. It was a thrilling moment, standing there, book in hand. It was worth all the aggravation we had gone through to have this tangible byproduct of my imagination. But I was not through paying for the privilege yet. Not by a long shot.

Now that we had books, we ramped up our marketing efforts. Leah contacted local bookstores and arranged for book signings and placement. We sent out a mass email and generated a landslide of instant book sales. Leah contacted the local media outlets and I did phone and live interviews for print publications.

With all the drama and the steep learning curves we had to plow through, things were now running quite smoothly. It was still a lot of work, maybe even more than before, because now it was about pushing the product and getting it to the marketplace while it was still fresh.

This was a good period for us publishing-wise. Things were happening and we felt very optimistic. We hadn't yet discovered how worthless our publicist was, but we realized we had to be as proactive as possible, strike while the momentum was there. The mood in the office was upbeat bordering on frantic; there had been another surge in loan business and we were all jamming.

Problem was, though I held it together as best I could, my body was falling apart. Having a lot to take my mind off the corporal helped, and I could usually push myself through working hours, but then I'd collapse in a heap of pain. My meltdowns were becoming more severe and more frequent, and it was becoming harder to keep up pretenses.

By the time my brother's wedding reception rolled around, I was barely functional. The thought of driving five-hundred miles to Nevada City would make me weak with dread. I couldn't do it. I was having trouble doing the bare minimum and I was nearly in a panic about making the trip.

Salvation came from Leah, who had the misfortune of having major dental work done. She knew I had taken prednisone and that it had helped. She decided she didn't need the dose the dentist had given her—the same 6-day pack Dr. N had prescribed. She gave me hers. It saved me, making the pain tolerable enough to take the three-day trip.

I rallied sufficiently to get through the whole experience and enjoy the time with my family, the dinner with all of us the night before the reception itself, which was held in a gorgeous, park-like setting.

It was there, during the festivities, that Guy got a call from Josiah. Justine had gone into labor that morning, a month earlier than expected. At one happy occasion we received the news of another: our first grandchild, Dashiell Diamond Hamilton, was born.

I was so grateful I hadn't missed these momentous occasions. Making sure whatever was wrong with me didn't steal my life away had been my constant goal. But I was almost at the end of my endurance.

Hope Springs Eternal

Unfortunately, life doesn't give you a time-out when you're ailing. Whatever is going on in your world doesn't go away until you're well; it just orbits around, taunting you. Smart people know that letting everything slide until you get better is an option. Either I'm too stupid or too stubborn, but not taking care of every little detail in my ridiculously over-crowded life never occurred to me. Everything *had* to be seen to, and with no half measures.

From here, I'm amazed and incredulous that I managed to do everything I did. It was insanity, driving myself like there wasn't anything wrong with me. I'd like to think it was because I didn't have a solid diagnosis, and therefore it was possible my symptoms were all in my head. But the truth is, nothing really changed after we got the Lyme results back. And in the middle of 2006, I was still months away from that shining moment of discovery.

In the meantime, though everyday seemed too painful to be real, I kept to the routine of office work, schlepping groceries up and down stairs, exercising, making lunch, doing all the errands, writing (book 5), buying sundries in bulk, cleaning up after strangers, cooking, cleaning, packing, unpacking, blah, blah, blah... Oh, and there was the book stuff. Can't forget that. Once that horse was out of the gate, there was no choice but to ride it to the end. Or fall off, which I eventually did.

It is a little painful to look back at the nitwit who was so deeply in denial and so deeply committed to holding everything together, no matter what toll it took. I'm torn between laughing and crying when I recall that every Sunday I'd wash my car up at Woodstock, before heading back down the mountain. *Why? Didn't I have enough to do?*

It's almost perverse that I fought an unseen enemy with such tenacity, my only weapon being my refusal to give up any part of my life. My nemesis had me on my knees, but I was going to make damn sure I cleaned the apartment every Thursday, whether it really needed it or not. And since I was already on my knees, I might as well scrub the grout—with a toothbrush.

But what can you do when your body no longer functions the way it used to? Just give up and give in? I think I clung to the chores and responsibilities of my life to keep from going under. I think I was afraid of falling down a hole of despair and never having the strength to crawl out again. If I let go of anything, it'd be all over.

Selling my book and the positive feedback I got from readers was like a gold filament that ran through my days. I never knew when someone was going to come up and tell me how much they loved the story of Allison and Jake.

I was interviewed for a publication called *The Valley Journal*, a free periodical that was distributed throughout Santa Barbara County. It was amazing publicity. At the time, it was published monthly, so the cover shot of me sat on the newsstands for a full month, generating a lot of encouraging comments from strangers.

I had a few book signings and more book club meetings, which I really enjoyed. I was doing everything I could to seize the moment and make the most of it. Plus, there was long-range planning to be done. It was always our strategy that we'd publish my other books, one by one, once we made a go of *Lucky*. But as good as things were going, I couldn't keep the charade up much longer; I had to get some relief. Soon.

I got another referral and worked up the requisite gumption to see rheumatologist #5. After seeing the last doctor, I had developed a theory I wanted to run by an expert who wasn't fixated on an erroneous diagnosis. For me, the only positive outcome of my last medical go-round was the elevated antinuclear antibodies.

High ANA results indicate that antibodies have become misdirected and are attacking healthy tissue, which is known as an autoimmune reaction. This condition results in connective tissue diseases, such as Lupus. Since a spike in my ANA level was the only abnormality to appear on the countless blood tests I had submitted to, it seemed logical to follow that lead, see if it would take us anywhere.

To prepare for meeting yet another new doctor, I put together an Excel spreadsheet, documenting my lengthy list of symptoms with a timeline of approximately when they appeared. To the best of my recollection, my problems started with the numbness and tingling in my extremities, hands and feet that turned blue when cold, unexplainable itching from head to toe. Then there were the rashes: cheeks, hands, eyelids. Dizziness, chills, lack of coordination, pain. Profuse pain of every description, in every part of my body—muscles, organs, joints, bones and skin. Trouble swallowing, racing heartbeat, digestive problems.

I looked up Lupus online and checked the box under each symptom I had that was associated with that disease. I then did the same for Fibromyalgia, which I had been diagnosed with twice. Lupus was the winner. It only covered some of my symptoms, but it does present with high ANA levels.

Of all the hypotheses over the years, this one seemed to make the most sense. I would take this spreadsheet to the new doctor, let him read the latest test results, and see if this made sense to him.

My first appointment with rheumatologist Dr. O went fairly well, except that I had forgotten my spreadsheet at my office. I gave him the verbal rundown as best I could remember, and asked his opinion of the ANA results. I explained all I had been through in the last seven years, all the blind alleys I'd been down without even a slight improvement in my symptoms. *Could it be lupus?* Dr. O equivocated, saying neither yes nor no.

When I told him my chief complaint was all the pain, his eyes lit up. *Did I have pain at night?* I told him that's when it was the worst. *Did I have pain in my legs? Did I move them around a lot?* Yes, I toss and turn a lot because of the pain. *You may have Restless Leg Syndrome!*

I couldn't believe what I was hearing. With all the symptoms I had trotted out for him, he wanted to talk about a hyped-up TV ailment, one of those convenient "syndromes" that weren't easy to document or explain.

He became very animated when he told me there was a sleep center at the clinic that could test me to see if I had RLS. I would need to spend the night, and they would hook me up to monitors, etc. I had a flash of worry that he was trying to pawn me off on some other department so he wouldn't have to deal with my can of worms. I told him I seriously doubted Restless Leg Syndrome was the cause of all my problems.

Dr. O looked a bit disappointed, but he acquiesced to treating me for lupus, for whatever good it could do. He explained that lupus is treated with anti-malarial drugs, and prednisone when there were "flares." *Ah, ha!* I thought: that's why I felt better when I took the prednisone. I told him I wanted to give the anti-malarial drug a try.

I can't recall how long it was before I started feeling better, but seemed to help pretty quickly. For three and a half months, I was convinced I had lupus and that the medication was working. I felt like a human being for the first time in years, not just a pain receptacle.

I saw Dr. O once during that time, as a follow-up to see how I was doing. At my second appointment, I detected a change in his demeanor toward me, which I couldn't account for. I was doing better on the medication; I thought doctors liked to hear that sort of news. Yet he seemed impatient and bored by my progress.

When the drug abruptly stopped working, I went back to see him. This time his manner was cold to the point of being snarky. I was hoping to find an explanation for why the drug worked for a while and then stopped, but our conversation was laborious and unproductive.

When I asked if there was another anti-malarial drug that might work better, he turned snide, telling me anti-malarial drugs are just antibiotics, and they aren't even used on malaria anymore. I didn't know what to make of this rebuke. He was the one who introduced me to "anti-malarials." If they're really antibiotics, why not call them that? And why was he so irritated with me?

The negative atmosphere in that office was hard to ignore. I left there feeling not only lost—no more treatment options—but also extremely pissed off by Dr. O's inexplicably hostile attitude. I was so upset and so irritated, I couldn't hide my rancor as I stood staring blankly at the elevators doors. "What an asshole!" I said to the vacant hallway. I cancelled my next appointment and never went to see him again.

WIT'S END

After my last disappointing visit with Dr. O, I found myself back where I'd started. I was disgusted with the thought of seeing another doctor, and had run out of reasonable options. I was still going through the pantomime of life, though it hardly felt like living. I was desperately trying to solve a problem that didn't seem to exist, and now I'd run out of medical options. Again.

The brief hiatus from pain became a tantalizing, elusive interlude that quickly receded from memory, like a footprint erased by an incoming tide. In a few short weeks, I couldn't even remember what it felt like to be pain free.

After so many years of dealing with an avalanche of debilitating symptoms, I was beginning to despair. I was broken down—physically, emotionally, psychologically. I was trapped by pain, by work, my lifestyle, my insane publishing scheme. As badly as I wanted to crawl down a hole and escape everything my life had become, I couldn't. There was no hole; there was no way to disappear.

The episodes of extreme pain became more frequent, leaving me a blubbering, incoherent mess. But as soon as the excruciating moments passed, I simply picked up where I'd left off. Those bouts of anguish did not earn me release; everything still had to be taken care of. There was no one who could handle my responsibilities except me.

Even while the wheels were coming off, I kept up my frantic pace. I have flashes of myself during that period and it almost makes me want to weep for that person who, from this vantage point, I hardly recognize. I wonder if I were face to face with myself as I was then, if I would be able to look past the exterior and see the inner turmoil. Or was it right on the surface, visible to everyone? It's hard to imagine that it wasn't, yet I know the plastic façade of wellbeing I hid behind fooled almost everyone.

A few weeks after the "anti-malarial" drug stopped working, I developed a new problem, one that came on out of nowhere and added a whole new layer of misery to my life.

Being situated in downtown Santa Barbara, everything we wanted was within walking distance: movie theaters, restaurants, bars, shopping—it was all right outside our doors. The new problem cropped up one evening after we bought our produce at the Tuesday farmer's market and stopped at a Thai restaurant for dinner on our way back to the apartment.

We had never eaten at this particular place and we weren't prepared for their level of spiciness. I've always loved spicy food. Hell, I love *all* food. Eating was one of my great pleasures, and almost a justification for living. And after my body started its revolt against me, food was my solace. But after this night, eating became a nightmare.

Though the dishes were definitely packing some heat, I didn't think too much of it—not until I woke up in the middle of the night breathing fire. I'm not talking about run-of-the-mill heartburn; I'm talking hydrochloric acid spewing up my throat and into my mouth. I felt sure that if I held a lit match in front of me, I could've breathed fire.

The pain was unlike anything I had experienced in that part of my body. I rummaged through the medicine cabinet, desperate to find something to put out the chemical fire. Nothing helped. I could feel the acid searing the lining of my esophagus on its way up. It was misery on top of misery. It was not okay.

For the next six weeks, I subsisted on white food—bread pudding, yogurt, oatmeal, rice, bananas—anything bland. It didn't make any difference. The acid kept pumping, despite the fact that I'd been on protease-pump inhibitors for six years. These magic pills didn't faze it.

I went to see Dr. J, the gastroenterologist; he had no new advice. I couldn't eat, couldn't have a well-deserved cocktail on the weekends. I was afraid of food and I was heartbroken to lose my only comforts. I sunk to a new level of despair. All the fun had gone out of my life.

I have a memory during that time up at Woodstock, when I just couldn't handle the pain load anymore, couldn't stand being in my body another second. I threw some sort of pathetic tantrum, more self-loathing than petulant, and stormed out of the house. This left me with two options: get in a car and drive away—or over a cliff—or, since I didn't grab any keys, walk. I walked. I stormed across the property, down the slope to the fence line.

It was a warm but windy afternoon, and I just stood out there, away from everything, and I cried. I had no options, no plan of defense, no escape hatch. I could walk for the rest of my life and never outrun my problems. I felt so defeated, so at my wit's end. I stayed out there, feeling very sorry for myself, willing a solution, a hope to spring into my head. Something. Anything.

As I stood out there in the high, dead grass, a song came to me, one that was on a playlist we listened to up at the ranch. I heard a different meaning in those words this time; they became a comforting promise that *"things are going to be easier...ooh, child things will be brighter..."*

The song welled up inside me, gave me the lifeline I'd been struggling to find. It became my lullaby, the thing I held onto when I closed up inside myself and tried to ride out the pain, waiting for the moment when things felt easier.

Though it seemed like an eternity to me at the time, a month and half after the onset, the acid problem went away. I had another 10-day bout with it, and then it completely disappeared for a couple of years. I don't have any recollection of rejoicing over this reprieve, probably because my other symptoms demanded so much of my attention, try as I did to ignore them.

The rest of 2007 was spent on book promotion, work, etcetera, etcetera. I attended a few more book club meetings, which I really enjoyed, though it took every ounce of strength and willpower to get through them.

In late September I participated in a disastrous book fair held in front of the Santa Barbara Library that was so poorly planned and executed, all I could do was count the hours until we could pack up and head back to the ranch. I sold books and smiled like a jackass and made it through the event without being accosted by vagrants, though others weren't as lucky.

The book fair was followed by a trip to Oakland for an annual event held to promote self-published authors. Set up was on Friday evening; Saturday and Sunday were spent talking to bookstore owners, publishers and agents. And handing out as many copies of *Lucky* as we could. Bless Guy for his dedication to me and my flagging aspirations. He was always by my side during the public events, promoting me and my book to anyone who would listen.

In November, I got a call from my brother. Brad would check in periodically to see how I was faring. This time, however, was different. This time he had a diagnosis for me.

Living up in the Mother Lode country of Nevada City, Brad had many massage clients with a wide range of peculiar symptoms, who had eventually been diagnosed with Lyme disease. He ran through a long list of afflictions, the aggregate sum of everyone's complaints.

"You have the same symptoms, but you have all of them," he said. "I really think you need to be tested for Lyme."

He had one client in particular who had shared her experiences from the very beginning, from the day she found the tick still attached to her skin. He thought I should give her a call.

After I got off the phone with Brad, I took a few moments to digest this possibility. *Wasn't I tested for Lyme?* Surely with all the countless vials of blood sucked from my veins someone must've checked for that. But what if they hadn't?

I called Rachael and we talked for two hours. She was so informative, it was almost too much to process. By the end of the call, I was overwhelmed—both hopeful and apprehensive. If I had Lyme, it was going to be a long, tedious road to recovery.

Having been an RN, Rachael attacked this situation like the medical professional she was. She went to a clinic to have the tick removed to be tested, but the nurse botched the removal and the test couldn't be performed. She was put on doxyclycline for 3 weeks, but it didn't work.

When she began having joint pains and shooting neurological pains, she had her blood tested. She learned that the lab with the highest accuracy rating was in Palo Alto, CA. She had her blood drawn and sent to the IGeneX lab. It came back positive.

Once she had her diagnosis, she started investigating what was known about Lyme disease and researching the leading doctors in the field, traditional and alternative.

She talked to a dozen people with Lyme before deciding to go with an alternative doctor in Arizona. She chose him because his protocol did not involve antibiotics and because, though he was treating Lyme with alternative methods, he had two board certifications: one in cardiology and one in internal medicine. Rachael was all for a non-antibiotic approach, as long as there was proof that it would work. Her motto was "show me the science." This doctor could.

When Rachael told me of her multiple visits to the clinic in Arizona and the 5–6 day stays there, seeing the doctor daily and undergoing various bizarre treatments, I felt bewildered. I couldn't imagine making the trip, let alone submitting to all the weird procedures. It all sounded too...unappealing.

Though seeing a parade of traditional doctors had done zero for me, I had trouble embracing the thought of "alternative" medicine. I had always thought of it as sort of a sham, turning my nose up at the unconventional methods, finding them a little too *oh wow*, airy-fairy, and downright suspicious.

Even though Rachael was very impressed by this doctor, I had trouble picturing myself going through all that. She told me that Dr. P had an uncanny ability to look into your eyes and find clues to your weak areas. Did I want a doctor looking so deeply into my eyes that he could root out all my hidden flaws? No. Did I want to get well? Yes.

But I was too intimidated by the thought of putting myself in the hands of someone who possessed almost psychic powers. I already had too much on my plate as it was; there was no way I was ready to deal with "issues." Not that Rachael had alluded to such thing. But still. "The past is there for a reason," has always been my credo.

Among the many things I learned from Rachael was that most of the standardized Lyme testing is fraught with a high percentage of false negatives. If I had been tested (and I would later learn I had been by Dr. B), there was a good chance the results were erroneous. She also told me testing too soon can also lead to an inaccurate result.

Rachael, like my brother, strongly urged me to take the alternative approach if Brad's hunch was correct. She advised me that from what she had learned, if Lyme isn't caught in the early stages, antibiotics aren't effective.

There are still doctors who believe that antibiotics can be used on late-stage Lyme, if they're administered through a PICC line (peripherally inserted central catheter) for a month or more, then switched to oral medication. But more and more experts believe they're not effective at that stage. Brad was totally against me taking them, believing that prolonged use would further suppress my immune system, not to mention what it would do to my digestive tract.

Hearing Rachael explain in detail what her protocol consisted of and how involved it was made my head swim. Dr. P used a battery of anti-microbial herbs to combat the spirochete—the insidious bacterium that causes the disease—plus a variety of vitamins, supplements and detoxing aids. The schedule was precise and required diligence. It was expensive, but so was the traditional method. And it would not be covered by insurance.

Rachael had been on her protocol for a few months, and though she had gotten her diagnosis and treatment early, she was already battling arthritis and iritis, a painful eye condition that can lead to blindness if untreated.

Rachael urged me to have a doctor order the test kit as soon as possible, as the results could take up to two weeks. When I expressed my reservations about traveling to Arizona, she told me of a doctor in Palo Alto who had attended seminars about treating Lyme given by Dr. P, and from what she gathered, he was pretty good. That was a relief. Driving up to Palo Alto was something I could handle, if I had to.

In the space of one afternoon, I had been given not only a good lead but also a game plan.

The only doctor I felt comfortable discussing this concept with was our primary care physician. Dr. Mesipam had taken over the practice when our former doctor, Dr. G, retired. I had seen Dr. Mesipam only once; he treated me for the bronchitis I picked up while hanging around the ER with Guy after a riding accident. I remember him having a very gentle, unhurried manner and Guy thought the world of him.

It had gotten to the point that I hated having to make my case to new doctors. The scenario had grown so long and unwieldy, it was always a challenge for me to sum it up in as few words as possible, getting to the crux without leaving out anything that might be useful. With Dr. Mesipam, my task was easier than I thought it'd be.

After summarizing Brad's theory and his directive to be tested for Lyme, Dr. Mesipam spoke up and said there was only one lab that properly knew how to test for it, and it was the same one Rachael told me about. Big sigh of relief; finally a doctor and I were on the same page.

My blood was drawn and sent to the lab in late November. Because of the Thanksgiving holiday, Dr. Mesipam was told it would take longer than usual to get the results. I started calling Dr. Mesipam's office in the second week of December: nothing back yet.

I called every week until Christmas, when his office was told it would be held up because of the holidays. Now that I had a chance to do a little research of my own, I was convinced this is what I had. But I'd been wrong before.

The long wait to find out the answer was excruciating. If I indeed had Lyme, I wanted to get started on treatment ASAP. I was on my last legs, barely able to make it through the day.

As Guy and I walked to Border's bookstore for my book signing in early December, I told him this would be the last thing I would be doing for the book. It was over, as far as I was concerned. Anything that would come from our publishing efforts after that would have to come on its own.

As a fitting end to my madcap scheme, this final event was nearly a complete fiasco, thanks to the Bookbastards.

When we got to Border's, I was greeted by the promotions manager. The books, which were promised weeks in advance of the signing, had just arrived a couple hours before. When he opened the box to set up the displays, he discovered that Bookbastards had sent softcovers, not the hardcovers the purchasing department had ordered. They couldn't even sell the softcovers because the SKU number wasn't the same, and it was too late to change it in the system. Thankfully, our office was only three blocks away.

While I was left there tap dancing, Guy ran back, threw a few cases of hardcovers into the car, and rushed them over. We were still setting up the table as customers came to get their copies. We were lucky to have had a decent turnout, as the delay in shipment didn't allow Border's to do any pre-event publicity.

After holding it together through the signing—which was great, in spite of Bookbastards—I felt myself crumble on the drive back to the apartment. I was completely spent. If the test results came back negative, I didn't know what I was going to do.

Now What?

Once we knew for sure what I was suffering from, Guy and Leah got busy on the internet. While I tried to assimilate my new status and deal with my office duties, I received links to various sites dedicated to Lyme. As I was soon to learn, there is a vast culture out there dealing with the illness.

Though there is a wide range of opinions regarding Lyme disease, most resources concur on the manifestation. Every symptom I had was listed, confirming for me the diagnosis: headaches, muscle aches, joint pain, irregular heartbeat, dizziness, chills, numbness and weakness in limbs, nausea, peripheral neuropathy, poor coordination, difficulty speaking, rashes, digestive problems, sore throat and trouble swallowing.

While a lot of those symptoms are present in other disorders, there is nothing else that encompasses them all. After recounting this litany of problems numerous times, it really baffled me that no doctor was able to see the correlation.

The more research we did, the more we discovered that Lyme is a highly debated disease, pitting the CDC against some physicians and practitioners. There is not only a split in how the disease is treated; there is also disagreement on where one can contract it. Many doctors still think only certain areas on the east coast are affected, while more and more are recognizing it's possible to be infected in all 50 states.

But as we were to find out, there is so much about Lyme that makes it hard to get a handle on. Lyme is the secret agent of the infectious diseases; it's able to shed its cell wall and infiltrate any part of the body, lying dormant until conditions are favorable, and going underground when it comes under attack. Lyme is a dirty double-crosser. Lyme is a bastard.

But at this point I had high hopes. Little did I know that finding a cure for late-stage Lyme was going to be as challenging as finding the cause of my symptoms.

Once I got off the phone with Dr. Mesipam, I told Guy and Leah, who both could tell by my reaction what the verdict had been. I guess to someone who didn't know the situation, my elation at finding out I had a horrible disease would've been quite suspect.

But Guy and Leah knew. They were just as relieved. So were my friends in the office next door, which is where I headed next. I felt like I should've been carrying a bouquet of red roses and wearing a crown after my triumph over misdiagnoses and incompetent physicians. I knew what was wrong with me! This was cause for celebration!

Guy went with me to see Dr. Mesipam the day after he phoned with the news. I was still basking in the euphoria of finally nailing what was wrong with me. Eight years it had taken to get to this point. Eight years—almost to the day—from my first doctor's appointment.

It didn't take long for the severity of what I was up against to unseat my unseemly jubilation. In Dr. Mesipam's office, it was time to figure out a treatment plan. Dr. Mesipam was appropriately somber, citing the long, arduous and uncertain road ahead of me. It didn't matter to him which path I took—traditional or alternative—but he would not be able to treat me, as he admittedly didn't know enough about the disease.

Dr. Mesipam had the name of a doctor he could refer me to; one of his other patients had Lyme and was seeing this M.D. He offered to contact his patient and see if she was willing to speak to me about her experience. She had been on antibiotics for six months and seemed to be improving.

Six months of heavy-duty antibiotics didn't really appeal to me, especially after the research I'd done. I could go that route and wipe out my immune system and my G.I. tract, only to find I was in worse shape, not better. And the thought of a PICC line—*yeesh.* No thank you.

Even though I was not enthusiastic about traveling to Palo Alto and submitting myself to who-knew-what kind of hocus-pocus, I still found the idea more palatable than using powerful drugs. At least everything would be natural, and being natural had it pluses. And hopefully there'd be no injectables.

I was able to get in to see Dr. Q at the end of January, just three weeks after my official diagnosis. I was glad I could start treatment so soon, but I was also still wary. I had no idea what I was going to encounter in Palo Alto, no idea what alternative medicine was really all about.

Acupuncture and chiropractic were as far from traditional medicine as I had ever strayed. I was used to the clean, bright offices, the impersonal staff, the long waits, the endless testing, the indifferent doctors, the dead ends...

Wait a second...why would I miss *that?* Maybe "alternative" would be better. It couldn't be worse, could it? After the long parade of M.Ds, it was my brother, the massage therapist/instructor, who properly diagnosed me. That fact alone gave me hope the alternative route was the way to go.

In preparation for starting the Lyme offensive, I was told I would need to have all my amalgam fillings removed. As Rachael had explained to me, Dr. P believed there was a relationship between Lyme and mercury, something about being a safe haven for Lyme to hide out in. I made an appointment with my dentist, Dr. R.

Dr. R was well aware of my health problems. Years before I got the Lyme diagnosis, I had gotten the idea my strange pains were the direct cause of old amalgam fillings leaking mercury into my bloodstream. I'd seen a piece on *60 Minutes* where several women with unusual ailments were able to finally trace them back to their aging dental work. *Did I have mercury poisoning?*

Dr. R examined my teeth and carefully explained why it was not possible in my situation. At the time, I was disappointed. It would've been so nice to find out the culprit and the solution in one office visit.

But now I had to explain to Dr. R that my old fillings had to come out, doctor's orders. Most of them were over 30 years old, and that alone was enough reason to replace them with non-amalgam fillings. Luckily, I only had about seven left.

We tackled the switch-out in two appointments. Dr. R, being the kind, gentle and thorough dentist that he is, felt duty-bound to point out there was a tiny speck of silver filling that had somehow burrowed its way up inside the tooth; removing it would destroy the tooth.

On the other hand, there was no way that any mercury could escape from where the filling was lodged. What did I want him to do? It was hard to imagine that little spot was going to prevent the treatment from working. I took the x-ray to show Dr. Q to get his opinion.

Guy was more up for the trip to Palo Alto than I was. After all the chaos of the last year, just getting away for a few days felt like a vacation to him. But I was still nervous about what I was about to embark on.

As soon as I entered Dr. Q's office, my apprehensions were confirmed. It was vintage hippie-dippie, with a garnish of hoity-toity, of the "please take off your shoes on the bamboo floor" variety.

The staff was mixed: part friendly, part disorganized, part frazzled. The waiting area, cramped and oddly furnished as it was, was enough to drive Guy out the door. Alone, I waited, picking up snatches of conversations, trying to gather clues as to what my appointment would be like.

After gazing repeatedly over the artifacts in the confined space—the wide selection of esoteric periodicals, the aquarium, the unusual artwork—for what seemed like an hour, the doctor finally called me in.

Dr. Q was shy and a bit awkward, which did nothing to alleviate my hesitant, awkward feeling. I followed behind as he led the way to his office-examination-treatment room, a space extremely cluttered with books, papers, boxes and odd artifacts. There was barely any space for me to sit. The air was stale; odors of past meals, burnt offerings, body odor and bad breath closed in on me immediately. There was a window, but it offered no fresh air and little light.

After a brief review of my history, Dr. Q unwrapped a collection of small vials on a massage table that did double duty as a countertop. He then had me stand. He placed one of the vials in my hand and had me hold out my left arm as firmly as I could, while he tried to force it down. This exercise was repeated dozens of times. After about fifty competitions of strength, I asked him if we could change arms, as my left one was about to fall off.

The purpose of this exercise—which is called muscle testing—was to determine which substances in this vast array of vials my body reacted negatively to. If Dr. Q was able to push my arm down, then I had an intolerance to whatever was printed on the bottle. What these bottles actually contained, I don't know, but they represented foods, plants, minerals and chemicals.

The muscle testing portion of the exam lasted an hour and a half. According to my performance, I was allergic to many things: pecans, eggs, brewer's yeast, onions, soy, beef, cane sugar, strawberries, cow dairy, oranges, pork, MSG, DDT, MEK, formaldehyde, iodine, fluoride, chlorine, phenol, all sulfas, and red, green and yellow food coloring. It was also determined during this session what types of antimicrobials my body reacted favorably to. I would take these to kill the Lyme.

After all the assessing was done, I was taken into another room where the doctor's assistant gave me a LAD treatment. This "Laser Acupuncture Detoxification" consisted of waving a pulsating light wand over me from head to toe. It wasn't painful or unpleasant, but it did seem a little odd. The assistant took it very seriously, protecting herself from my cooties with a white sheet.

By now I was realizing I had landed in Alternative Central. If I still had any reservations about leaving normal to venture into the medical hinterlands, it was too late; I was now into it up to my neck—and then some.

As daunting as all this was, it was tame compared to the take-home instructions. I was sent back to the hotel with enough bottles and jars to fill two grocery bags. When I finally emerged from the office two and a half hours later, I was dazed and confused. After stopping at the grocery store to retool (my toiletries were no longer safe for me), we headed to our hotel room.

Once settled, I began reading through several sheets of instructions for the stuff I had to start consuming, per the regimented schedule.

The post-LAD instructions had me in a dither as I tried to comply with the unreasonable and complicated orders.

I couldn't use lotions, makeup, deodorant, etc. for a 25-hour period. Two hours before and twenty-four hours after the treatment, I couldn't eat anything I was allergic to, plus caffeine, mint and cinnamon. I was supposed to stay 8 feet away from all electronic devices. All electronic devices. I felt panicky as I looked around me; electronics were everywhere—there was no way to avoid them.

As I started to unpack my new regimen, I became totally bewildered. The task in front of me was completely overwhelming. I began lining up all the bottles, trying to organize them according to the order in which they were to be taken.

There were thirty bottles of capsules, compounds, liquids and powders. I remembered Rachael mentioning some of these "remedies," but I had no clue how arduous this process was going to be. I was starting to have serious reservations about this alternative business; having toxic drugs injected into my bloodstream was starting to look more appealing.

The following morning I was up at dawn, desperately trying to take all my stuff in the proper order. There were drops that had to be taken in water 15 minutes before eating, drops to be taken 30 minutes after eating, drops to take twice a day, and drops to take four times a day. By the time I got the first half of the day's doses in me, I was a nervous wreck.

To add to my anxiety was the thought of having to go out into the world without benefit of the blow dryer and curling iron, deodorant and makeup. In the afternoon, I humbly submitted myself to round two of the Kill Lyme offensive.

The next day, we packed up and headed home. It was a somber drive for me; I didn't know how I was going to get through this treatment. I felt guilty, as though I had chosen this awful disease and unreasonable treatment regimen. Figures I'd have some sort of kink to my diagnosis.

A strange thing happened on the drive home. When we stopped for gas, I went to use the restroom. When I got back to the car, the reek of gas fumes almost knocked me out. It smelled as if Guy had flooded the backseat with gasoline. I asked him when he got back in the car if he had leaked any fuel when he was filling up. He said no, not a drop. After we got home, I read in my instructions not to fill my car with gas for at least 24 hours after treatment. It gave me an eerie feeling to find proof there might be something to this weird approach after all.

Late-stage Lyme is entirely different than Lyme caught early. What I wasn't quite getting at the time was how slim my chances were of actually being cured. If I had known then what I know now, I would've curled up and died right then and there. But this visit to Palo Alto was just the tip of the alternative iceberg.

WIT'S END, PART II

Somewhere between writing *Alligators* and publishing *Lucky*, I started working on Book 5. My inspiration for this novel was taken from an unfinished compound Guy and I often drove by on our trips into Santa Ynez. For years we had passed this work-in-progress, speculating on what it was and if it would ever be finished.

For some reason, I was intrigued by the oddity of a project made up of several structures large enough to be houses, yet too close together to be separate properties. It looked more like a family compound than a business venture. My mind compulsively invents stories with little more than a snapshot to go on, and after years of contemplating possible scenarios, I finally decided to let my imagination run with this one.

Despite the thin premise, I concocted an intricate plot involving a small town in Northern California besieged by a recent spate of arson-caused wildfires. I threw in a newly divorced mother and her two young children who settle there out of financial necessity, and three generations of Wilbrands who strive to finish and occupy a compound directly across the street.

I combined all the elements, cut off Uncle Jess' hand, gave Jared (the youngest Wilbrand) a love of nature and a special interest in birds, and Race Wilbrand (father and nephew) the heavy burden of trying to finish the family compound without the requisite funds.

Since the fires played an important part in the story, firefighters played supporting roles. One in particular divides his free time between trying to cozy up to Caroline, the divorcée, and making life miserable for Race, who out of desperation, is forced to do odd jobs wherever he can find them.

Caroline, who has come down significantly in the world, has bought a house that needs all the fixing up Race can give it. Her two spoiled children are now getting a crash course in how the world outside of Encino lives. They are entranced by young Jared, who shows the city kids a side of life they've never seen.

And meanwhile, the fires continue…and a crafty arsonist remains at large, keeping the small community in a constant state of unease.

I pursued this book the way I did the four previous: writing furiously for a few hours on weekends. And as with the other novels, *The Heroes of San Benicio* was shaping up to be another lengthy one. Despite my decrepitude, I forced myself to write whenever time permitted, no matter how lousy I felt.

I had been writing for six years, and I was certain that if I were to abandon my writing, I would lose the discipline I had worked hard to cultivate. As with everything else in my life, I was determined Lyme would not steal away pieces of who I was. I was sure if I let go of anything, it would become a downhill slide.

But now I had a new item to add to my overburdened plate: the cumbersome and tedious Lyme regimen, which asserted itself as top priority, along with all the other top priorities. Now when we made the schlep to and from Woodstock, I had a large tote full of my extensive protocol to lug around. Just one more layer of stuff to deal with.

Wherever we happened to land, I had to fish everything out of the bag and arrange it on various surfaces according to how and when each thing had to be taken. Getting used to the schedule took diligence. I felt like I was performing some farce to amuse the fates, measuring this, timing that. It felt ridiculous and it was a pain in the ass. It added a new level of stress to the mix and made me even more apprehensive about the viability of what I had signed on for.

To further complicate matters, I was told to eat only foods listed for type A in *The Blood Type Diet*. I was given a photocopied list from the book, though naturally, Guy had to go buy a copy for ourselves.

Reading *The Blood Type Diet* became kind of a parlor game for Guy and Leah, who were lucky enough to be born with type B blood. Could they stick to this diet? Sure, no problem. They got to eat all the fun stuff, while I was stuck eating mostly fruits and vegetables. I love fruits and vegetables, but I'm a born carnivore. I don't care what anybody says; I don't just love meat, I *need* it.

There might be some interesting theories behind this diet, maybe even some sound science, but I think most of us know what foods are best for us. Besides, I didn't need to lose weight. But despite my justifications for not following through with it, for the month between my first and second visits to Palo Alto, I stuck to the diet, and I was miserable.

My second visit to Dr. Q was more of the same, plus a few new assignments. I was told to make a paste of powdered Bentonite clay and one of my elixirs, rub it on my scars and let it sit for ten minutes, wash it off and repeat the whole process twice more. I was to do this three days in a row.

I was also told to purchase a "rebounder," which is a small trampoline. The reason for this was to get my lymph system moving. Apparently, it wasn't, and dead Lyme cells were starting to back up all over my body.

Dutiful and committed, I went online and bought one. After lugging it back and forth a few times, I bought another one: one for the apartment and one for Woodstock. I actually found bouncing to be quite stimulating; it made me feel giddy and slightly lightheaded, and it made me smile. Soon, I wasn't the only bouncing fool in the office. I got Guy and Leah both hooked.

I was also advised to have ionic footbaths. As I discovered once I started calling around, I wasn't the only person who had never heard of them. I finally found a salon in Summerland that offered them. My sister Melanie and I tried the experiment together. The sessions lasted about an hour, during which time our feet soaked in cool water, which eventually turned all kinds of colors as nasty toxics seeped out.

According to the color chart, I was exuding heavy metals, which was the black stuff, and the wispy rust color supposedly came from the joints. Melanie turned her water a foaming brackish-green, which signified gallbladder issues. Though the experience was interesting, I didn't feel any differently afterwards. But poor Mel was not so lucky; she turned about as green as her foot bath.

In March, after my second trip north, I began to feel increasingly worse. I think the Lyme killing had started in earnest by then. All my normal pains were exaggerated, revved up. I would lie on the bed and marvel at the depth and breadth of the pain. It was hard to even assess it all. As I lay there, my attention would focus on the most vicious of the ragged bolts that zinged from one end of my body to the other.

And there wasn't just ragged bolts; there was jackhammering in my temples, jolts of electric current shooting through my toes, stabbing pains throughout my organs. Tiger claws down my back. Steamrolled hands and feet. None of this was new, but now the intensity pushed the agony index over the top.

For years I had mental images of what my body looked like on the inside. When I closed my eyes, I could see bursts of color as the pain pinballed around, banking and rebounding, crossing paths with oncoming balls of fury. It was almost as if I had the aurora borealis trapped inside me.

As the pain pulsated, so did the lightshow. Even though I was supposed to be resting, the bombardment of these sensations and the pain left me exhausted. Every day brought a different color palette, as though whatever pain sequence I was experiencing had its own corresponding colors and designs, sometimes appearing kaleidoscopic, sometimes like a lava lamp. If it wasn't the visual accompaniment to a body blasting, I would've found it enchanting.

Over the years, I had asked doctors if there was a way to gauge a person's pain levels. I had been hoping there was some new technical devise that would, when attached to a body, light up when it sensed pain. If such a thing existed, doctors would then be able to grasp what was going on in their patients' bodies. I knew that if I were hooked up to such a contraption, I would light it up like a Christmas tree. Then they could see where the pain was. Then they would have proof of what was going on. Then they would believe me.

I have a memory of a recurrent image I would often have up at the ranch. The vision was like a painting, an abstract. There were two people, a man and a woman, posed as if they were at a cocktail party or a gallery opening. Their bodies were featureless silhouettes filled with brilliant shades, scribbles of colors overlapping and frenetic, as though you could see the life force inside them.

Facing these two people was another featureless figure, this one bursting with heavy black scrawls, tangled and jagged, nearly filling the outline. It appeared as if this person was rotted and dead inside.

This person was me. This was how I felt, as though I was no longer the same as anyone else. I was one of the walking dead, set apart, unable to remember what it felt like to be a human being, to be me.

The next several months were a downward spiral. What I was feeling was to be expected when killing Lyme. As Lyme cells die, they become toxic, setting off a worsening of one's symptoms. For me, this included more body aches, nausea, chills, and a heightening of the overall pain. This process is referred to as a Herxheimer's reaction.

On one hand, I had to appreciate the fact that we were getting the bastards. Yet I couldn't help but think I was getting worse than I was giving. Lyme is just such a resilient, crafty son-of-a-bitch, mutating when it experiences a drop in its numbers, lying low until the assault is over. This is why drugs and herbal equivalents are administered with pauses and are rotated after these short breaks in order to keep the Lyme off-kilter.

During this time, I finally had to face the fact that I was no longer able to write. I kept it up as long as I could, dragging my sorry carcass up the spiral staircase to sit in my writing chair with my laptop.

But the exercise had become fruitless; my fingers were mutinying, flailing over the keypad, completely disobeying my orders. It would take me so long to write one paragraph, having to hit the backspace key after every second or third letter, often multiple times per letter. Within half an hour, the pain in my spine and hands was excruciating. It was no use.

I had written 70,000 words and was about halfway through *San Benicio*, at the point where I had to start pulling all the plotlines together as I wove the story to the conclusion. But I had to abandon it and all the characters I had created. I didn't have the wherewithal to see it through. I was defeated. It was the first time I had ever given up on anything, and it just about broke what little spirit I had left.

There was one Thursday in particular I remember for the extra-high levels of pain and the extra-low level of fortitude. It was all I could do to get through the requisite cleaning, packing, schlepping, unpacking and preparing for dinner. I had been pretty stoic during all the years I was besieged by pain, but there were occasions when I just couldn't hold it together any longer. This evening was one of them.

All day I had kept focused on the idea of sitting in my comfy chair by the roaring fire, flipping through magazines and catalogs, the only time waster I indulged in. But once I got up there, I was hurting too much to even sit. I just wanted out of my body. There was no way to find any comfort.

I could feel a breakdown coming, so I went into the bathroom and started to wash my face, which was a good cover to hide the blubbering. But letting the sadness out didn't relieve the pressure; it only made me feel worse.

As I stood there over the sink, staring at my woeful features in the mirror, I had to come to terms with what I was feeling. I had reached a point where I couldn't imagine suffering through another day like this one. I had to articulate in my mind what I had never wanted to admit. I needed to stop this life, stop the pain, stop my anguish. The question was, could I do it?

I had been this low before and not been able to face the obvious. Those incidents were behind me, but their accumulation was what made this particular episode so compounded. How many more days like this would I have to endure? Did I really have that much inner stamina to face them? Why should I put myself through this...through everything, if all I had to look forward to was continual decline?

But the bigger issue was the same question I had wrestled with before: could I really end my life? Could I kill myself? I had the desire, the deep need to be freed from the torture. But it always came down to two things: being a quitter and hurting those I would be leaving behind. This time though...this time I had to find the strength. And I had to find the means.

As I consulted my ravaged visage, I contemplated how to do it. What would be the best way? What would be the kindest exit? As I grasped at possibilities, something odd happened. Where there had been nothing but despair in my soul, a small flame of creative curiosity sprang to life. I could see it all in my mind's eye: a woman found dead in her bedroom chair, a syringe lying by her feet. Was it suicide? Or was it murder???

A plot raced through my head as my expression in the mirror turned to one of surprised joy. It would be a murder mystery. A pair of detectives sprung to mind, along with the grieving husband. The woman had been a journalist for twenty years, chasing down corrupt politicians and crooks alike. There could be lots of people with a vendetta to square.

And there was another angle: the woman had been suffering for several years from Lyme disease. Maybe she had taken her own life, or maybe it had been a mercy killing, or...

Though I had stopped working on *San Benicio*, I rationalized that starting fresh might be easier. It would be less taxing to not have to weave that complicated plot to the conclusion. Starting from the beginning is always exciting, and this was a subject I knew intimately. It would be fun and it would keep me focused on something besides myself. I would do it! I would turn the tables on Lyme. I would not take the easy way out.

Despite my initial enthusiasm and a promising start, I realized after 10,000 words that typing for extended periods was out of the question. I got the brilliant idea to buy a handheld voice recorder, but by the time it arrived, I was so far gone, I didn't have the wherewithal to use it. I had to let go of writing for the second time.

How Much Worse Can It Get?

There's one phrase I've learned never to utter: *What next??* I frequently found myself saying this, and eventually realized I was only tempting fate. Every time I thought things couldn't get worse, they did.

It's really hard to remember everything going on during that time; in fact, I almost forgot a very troublesome footnote to this especially trying period. It would've been gross enough if it had only been the one incident, but as repulsive as it was, it was merely a hint of things to come.

The day before we were scheduled to drive up to Palo Alto for another doctor visit, we left the ranch to go back to the apartment for the night. On the way down the driveway, Guy stopped to put the garbage cans out on the street.

While he was doing this, I reached into the glove compartment to get him a wipe for his hands. As soon as I looked inside, I had this terrible feeling come over me. *Where did all this weird furry stuff come from?* This did not look good.

Furry tan poufs spilled out as I gingerly moved the contents of the glove compartment. I felt the sheepskin seats, searching for holes. Even though I couldn't find any, it became obvious that something had been building a nice, woolly nest.

Guy came back to the car as I was ripping everything out and tossing in on the ground, where I could further inspect it. I found the wipes and frantically began to scour every surface and every item I deemed important enough to keep. *Oh, yuck!* I thought. *How disgusting! Mice, in my car!*

The forty-five minute drive into town was spent wondering if we had stowaways. The cat, who is cross-eyed and was orphaned young, is not much of a mouser, and was curled up in his carrier anyway. Even if he had been a mouse-catching expert, the pass is harrowing enough without having a cat and mouse chase in progress. But I kept looking back at him, checking for signs that he had smelled a mini rat.

We stopped at the store to pick up some traps, just in case. We thought we were overkilling it a bit with the quantity of traps we bought, but we weren't going to take any chances. The drive over the pass was unnerving enough; there was no way we were going to travel the 350 miles to Palo Alto accompanied by vermin.

The next morning, I came down to do an inspection before Guy brought our luggage down. I hazarded a glance through the window at the passenger side floorboard. *Oh joy, we got it!* I thought, as I pulled on rubber gloves to remove the revolting creature. I flung the trap into the garbage bag and breathed a sigh of relief. It was over.

I went to the back of the Jeep to get the boxes so I could put the unused traps away. To my horror, I found another dead mouse. I extracted it and threw it in the bag with the first. Now I was afraid to open the back doors. *There can't be more,* I thought as I steeled myself and looked inside. *Oh, crap! Why didn't I get Guy to do this?* I opened the door. Two more mice lay dead in the sticky traps. With much trepidation, I got them out and reunited them with the others.

We had two more traps that hadn't been occupied, so I left them where they were. If it were possible to have more mice, I wanted to make sure we caught the little monsters. I tried to convince myself we had gotten them all, just for sanity's sake.

I went up to the apartment and grabbed disinfectant and lavender spray and cleaned every surface I could before we brought bags down. The good news was that the traps remained empty during our trip. *Whew,* we thought; that was lucky.

As things got more difficult for me, I started thinking of ways to simplify our life. Oddly, it was other efforts at simplification that had made our life so overly-complicated.

Woodstock had become a sanctuary for me; it was the opposite of work. That's what it represented for me, more than anything else. Guy still worked on Fridays up at the ranch, but I didn't. There was nothing work-related I could do without being in the office. Guy could work anywhere he had a phone, computer and his HP calculator.

Our time was evenly divided between our office/apartment and the ranch. We got up to Woodstock on Thursday afternoons and usually left on Monday mornings.

Because I spent so much time up at the ranch, and because taking care of Summerland between tenants had become an extra burden I could've done without, I started talking to Guy about the possibility of improving the ranch—adding a large barn with an apartment down at the foot of our property—and selling Summerland. If we had sleeping accommodations at the ranch to handle our growing family and still had the apartment downtown, we wouldn't really need Summerland anymore.

Guy liked the idea. The ranch was a very special place to him. I think he could've been happy with Woodstock and nothing else. So it didn't take much persuading to get him fired up about building a barn/apartment. I drew up some sketches to get an idea of how much space we had and the best use of it. Guy contacted an architect who came out and walked the property with us.

After eliminating the best location on the ranch because of the added driveway costs it would trigger, we opted for the original placement. The architect then drew up the plans. We were both very excited by how this addition would enhance the property. We were anxious to get started, but we had one major hurdle to cross first, and that was selling Summerland. We put the project on hold temporarily while we contemplated our next move.

Our house in Summerland was now 20 years old and had been used for the last 3 years as a vacation rental. If we wanted to get top dollar for it, we were going to have to spruce the place up first. Our contractor and his foreman came to the house and went over the things that needed to be replaced and upgraded. I thought of this process as more of a fact finding mission than anything else. We were in no hurry. Besides, we had plenty on our plates as it was.

A couple days later, Guy poked his head inside my office and told me he was meeting the painter at Summerland.

"You're just getting a bid, right? We're not going to start doing anything yet...right?"

"Oh, yeah—that's all," he assured me. He returned a couple hours later and informed me that the painters were starting the next morning. I was flabbergasted.

"But I haven't even picked out any paint colors," I said, bewildered by his rash act.

"Well, you'll have to go over there first thing tomorrow and sort that out. They've already started moving everything into the garage."

I went over to the house the next morning after stopping to pick up some paint chips. When I got to Summerland, nearly all of the contents of the house were packed into the garage, with barely a trail to squeeze through.

The painters were all over the house; two boom boxes set to different Mexican stations blared at full blast. All the windows were already covered in plastic. All the lamps were out in the garage and it was an overcast day outside, which meant I had a very hard time trying to gauge which paint colors would work best.

Unfortunately, my eyesight had been deteriorating the past several weeks. I had a pair of Guy's cheater glasses with me, but even with them on, I couldn't read the names of the paint chips. It was ridiculous to try to choose colors under these conditions, but I had been told our job had been squeezed in and painting had to begin the next day.

I borrowed a fan deck from one of the painters and did my best to match paint swatches to rooms. Then I went back to the paint store— a total of three times—and bought various cans of paint, went back to Summerland, brushed on samples and tried to make decisions. I tromped through the house, in the way of the crew as they laid plastic over everything.

A week later, the painters were finished and everything had been restored to its proper place. Now we had to concentrate on picking out granite for the kitchen counters, door hardware, toilets, appliances, mirrors, bathroom tiles, window coverings, etc. In two months, all the work was done and everything was in place. It wasn't a full remodel, but it was perfectly calculated facelift. Now we had to work on the outside...

When we first started work on the house, there were two homes in Summerland for sale. When we finished the interior, there were thirteen. After all the time and money we had spent, we knew it would've been foolish to add another listing to the pile. We decided to hold off on the exterior improvements and wait for the inventory to thin out.

Unfortunately, it didn't. More and more properties came on the market in the weeks following our half-rehab. In spite of our desires, it became obvious we would need to keep renting Summerland out. So much for the barn idea. So much for simplification.

After the third trip to see Dr. Q, I took a decided turn for the worse. My vision got so bad, I could barely see to do my work, with my glasses on. I had to use a magnifying glass and my reading glasses to see the dollar amounts on the escrow closing statements. When I got to the point where I couldn't tell the color of my eyes in the mirror or read the instrument dials on my dashboard, I scheduled an appointment with the ophthalmologist.

I hadn't been to see Dr. S since I had been diagnosed with Lyme. Fortunately, he was familiar with the disease and its effects on the eyes. Dr. S tested my vision and dilated my eyes to check for problems. There was no iritis or any other damage. Nor was he able to see any Lyme cells. I was glad for that, but it didn't explain my sudden vision impairment.

I called Dr. Q and explained the situation. The problem, he said, was that my liver wasn't processing the dead Lyme cells fast enough and they were backing up where they died. Since the cells become toxic when they die, this was making my symptoms worse. He increased the dosage of two of my formulas.

Three days later, my legs collapsed as I got out of bed. I got to my feet, but I could barely stand. I lurched and crashed my way to the nearest seat. I was in so much pain, I was at the point of giving up. I couldn't take this deterioration anymore.

When the cat begged to be let out the bedroom door, I opened it and closed it behind him. I didn't care that he could've been eaten by a coyote. I didn't care about anything anymore. Guy was horrified at my indifference to our cat's well-being; this had to mean I was really suffering if our precious baby's safety no longer mattered to me. Nothing did at that point. I staggered into the living room where I could lick my wounds in private.

As I sat there feeling absolutely abysmal, I belatedly noticed that I'd been unconsciously reading the cover of a magazine on a table two feet away. Whereas I couldn't even read the three-inch title before, I discovered I could now read every word on the cover, even the teeny-tiny print at the bottom.

I jumped up, overjoyed by this sudden turn of events. I could see! I could really see! My vision hadn't been this clear in four years. My surly attitude instantly evaporated. It was a miracle!

The joy and new optimism I felt transformed me. The treatment was working. Dr. Q knew what he was doing. I was going to beat this disease. I would get well again.

Now I looked forward to taking all the strange stuff I hauled from place to place. I looked upon Carnivora—the powdered version of the Venus flytrap, reputed to devour dead Lyme cells—as my best friend. I had a new respect for the glutathione, Takuna, Cumanda, D-ribose, L-carnitine, R-lipoic acid, CO Q 10, burbur, bromelain, etcetera, that I forced down my gullet every day.

As strange as it all was, this is what I had opted for over conventional medicine. And the good news was it wasn't all claptrap, as part of me had feared. I could now see the results for myself. Literally.

Once the vision problem cleared up, I became more patient toward my protocol. So I wasn't able to resume writing; that would come in good time. I had written four books with no more than a two-week break in between. It was okay that I wasn't pushing myself; I didn't have any deadlines to meet.

Somewhere along the road I had made peace with the fact that my self-publishing days were behind me. I'd taken my big chance, but my timing wasn't exactly great. I had to admit to myself an undertaking of that proportion was not possible when you are very sick. I suppose I had become as Zen as I was ever going to be. I was just going to work on getting well and take everything else as it came.

Even though I had given up writing, the time I had allotted toward it was swallowed by all the other demands in my life. Once I had taken it out of the equation, I didn't think about the discipline I had given up; I didn't dare. I just looked forward, and not very far into the future.

Having eased the pressure I put on myself, I enjoyed being up at Woodstock more. I puttered around in the garden with the cat, walked as much as I could, and enjoyed the warm summer weather once it finally arrived.

One of the benefits of being up at the ranch was spending time with our neighbors. Carlos and Dottie Spencer, who owned the property adjacent to ours, became our close friends. We would take turns cooking for one another, always delighting in our good fortune of having such great neighbors.

On the 4th of July, 2007, at 10:30 in the morning, I saw a plume of smoke billowing up into the sky. It looked very close. I called to Guy, who brought out the binoculars. He called Carlos, and together they went to the top of Carlos and Dottie's property to get a better view. It *was* close. They got on the phone and found out that a fire had broken out at a ranch less than five miles away.

We had watched the fire grow and the smoke expand its territory for several hours before heading next door. As we drove down our driveway in the Kawasaki, we were jittery about the direction the fire would take. It would be nothing for the blaze to blow straight into Woodstock. It was summer; everything was dry. The ranch between La Laguna and Woodstock had lots of dry brush. The whole area could become an inferno in a matter of hours.

At Carlos and Dottie's 4th of July party, more facts emerged. The fire had started moments before I saw the smoke. Two ranch hands were trying to repair a water trough with a grinder right as the winds started to pick up. A spark jumped from the containment area, quickly igniting the parched, knee-high grass. Despite the frantic efforts of the workers, the blaze was out of control within seconds. Crews arrived from across the valley; in the time it took to get there, it was clear this was going to be a formidable fire.

The Zaca Fire, as it came to be known, thwarted all efforts to bring it under control. While we were at the Spencer's house, we hoped the fire crews had been able to put it out. As soon as we rode up to our house, we knew that wasn't the case.

From the top of our driveway we could see the smoke that had wafted our direction and been sucked down into the canyon behind our house. It hung there ominously, a thick reminder of how close the danger was.

When we left to go back to the apartment, we did so not knowing if our property would be spared. The fire had grown horrifically large, yet it had so far defied logic and moved toward the mountains instead of heading east, where many homes and ranches would have been threatened.

Back at the office, we got daily updates from our neighbors. No good news yet; the fire was still raging. Our friend Jeanne told us about a conversation she'd had with one of the fire inspectors. He told her "the powers that be" would probably let this fire go until it consumed 100,000 acres. We all had trouble believing the fire would ever get that big. How could it? How could they just let it go? They were actively fighting it; surely they could stop it soon.

Come Thursday afternoon, we headed back up. The fire had consumed tens of thousands of acres and containment was nowhere in sight. We couldn't believe what was happening; the fire had made a wide arc around us and was moving east. At any time, the winds could change course, blowing the fire back toward us.

Meanwhile, Santa Barbara and communities to the south of us were being inundated by heavy smoke and ash—ash so thick, it piled up on everything in Santa Barbara. Cars, buildings, trees, streets—everything was covered in ash. Up at the ranch, the air quality was fine. Nothing about this fire made sense.

By the time I made the trip up to Nevada City to see my family, 80,000 acres had been scorched. The news continued to be more of the same while I was gone; raging fire, but everything at Woodstock was fine. It was surreal. The smoke could be seen way off in the distance, past the coastal range, hovering like dark, sinister fog.

One weekend in mid-August, the winds shifted. For the first time in six weeks, the valley air was now heavy with smoke and ash. Normally, we could look out the eastside windows and see Figueroa Mountain, the valley and the Coastal Range clearly. But that weekend, the air was brown, hanging close to the ground, acrid and full of ash. It was impossible to be outside at all.

Guy and I drove to Buellton to see a movie, just to get out of the house. We cut our stay short, hoping conditions in Santa Barbara were better. As it was hot, I watered the potted plants outside and brought all the cushions in. Other than that and taking stuff from and to the car, I didn't spend any time out in the smoke.

Two days later, back at work, I started having a bad headache. It was different than my usual headaches; this one made my whole face hurt. Leah and her family had gone to Florida for a week, so I was "it." I was handling her job and mine, but I was having a hard time functioning. I kept taking stuff for the pain, but nothing helped. I had the headache all through the night, and woke up with it the next morning.

By the third day, I could barely stand the pain. My entire head and everything in it throbbed: my teeth, eyeballs, the bones in my face, my jaws. My throat, the roof of my mouth, my tongue and lips burned. My whole head felt like it was going to explode.

Even though I was the only staff on duty, I had to leave my post periodically to go lie down in the back. Through all the years of being sick and having a bed I could go to when I felt terrible, this was the only time I'd ever done it. I knew this was more than just a really bad headache. When blood started gushing from my nose, I knew I was in trouble.

I was in too much agony to go in search of comfort. Whatever could be done to make me feel better, Guy was going to have to do it. Unfortunately, Guy was busy with work. I lacked the ability to get my cell phone out of my purse just six feet away, so I laid there, waiting until he was free to come check on me.

While lying there, I remembered that the questionnaire I filled out for the Lyme test had a box to check if the patient had encephalitis. That box was one of only three out of 25 that I didn't check off. But now I had to wonder. Wasn't encephalitis swelling of the brain? That would make your head feel like it was going to explode, for sure. When Guy finally came to the back, I asked him to look up encephalitis online.

When he brought me what he had printed off the internet, I realized I had a lot of the symptoms, fever being one of them. One site pointed to Lyme disease as a cause. I asked him to see if he could get me an appointment with Dr. Mesipam.

We got a 5:00 appointment, the last of the day. When we walked into the office, we could tell by the number of bodies in the waiting room that some of us were going to have to wait. As time passed, we were able to piece together that there was another crisis situation underway. When a nurse we knew joined the party, we realized something was seriously wrong with the woman in with Dr. Mesipam.

By 6:00, the pain had me in tears. Once the dam broke, I couldn't hold it back. I wasn't sobbing, but tears poured out of my eyes, as if something inside my head had to be released to lessen the pain. I could barely breathe due to the reverberations it would set off in my brain. Guy found a box of Kleenex and sat beside me to shelter me from view as we waited for the doctor to appear.

Dr. Mesipam had never seen me in such bad shape. I was a wreck by the time we were called into his office. I could barely walk, and when I tried to speak, I stuttered and sputtered and was barely coherent. Dr. Mesipam was concerned about the possibility of it being encephalitis and wanted my head checked out right away.

Because it was 6:20 on a Friday, he had to send me to the emergency room. He phoned the doctor on call at Goleta Valley Hospital, knowing that it even though it was farther away, it would be less of a zoo.

This time it was Guy's turn to endure all the joys of the emergency room experience as a caretaker, not the patient. It's hard to believe, but we didn't leave the hospital until 11:30 that night. I was shown to an examining area fairly early in our visit, but I had to lay there as the doctor dealt with the patients ahead of me. Because the "rooms" were partitioned off with drapes, I couldn't help but listen to the conversations of those in need around me. Emergency rooms are never happy places.

By the time Dr. T came to deal with me, I think I was suffering empathy pains on top of everything else. I certainly didn't feel any better, let's put it that way. She'd had the heads up from Dr. Mesipam, and after some routine questions and a quick check of my vitals, she offered me a painkiller of my choice.

I'd had morphine before when I had a kidney stone, and that had worked just dandy. But for some reason that I can't remember, it wasn't a good option. I went instead with the most potent anti-inflammatory on the market. She gave me an injection, then the nurse came in to prep me for a CT scan of my brain.

Time passed and Dr. T returned. The CT scan didn't show what they were looking for; she needed to do a lumbar puncture. From listening to her in action, I could tell she was quite competent. I could also tell she was a little nervous about giving me a spinal tap in my current condition. She reassured me and I reassured her. I told her I'd had one before and I knew I had to lie perfectly still. I'd be okay.

Guy left the room as Dr. T began the procedure. The painkiller had still not kicked in at this point, though it had been hours. The nurse came in to assist, and the doctor got me positioned to start the lumbar puncture.

I laid still and everything went fine. I didn't really feel anything. I couldn't move anyway because of what was going on in my head. When the doctor finished, she told me she had never seen anyone handle a lumbar puncture so perfectly. She said I was the all-time champ. I think she was trying to cheer me up.

The spinal fluid was rushed off to be examined. More waiting. Sometime later, Dr. T returned; there was no sign of encephalitis. That was the good news. But it didn't tell me what was causing all the pain. Right before we checked out, the Toradol started working. I was told to have a follow up with Dr. Mesipam on Monday to go over the results of the tests.

The shot I got in the hospital, though late to kick-in, lasted two days. In fact, I hadn't felt that good in ages. But by Monday, the exploding head was back.

Dr. Mesipam explained that Toradol was the strongest anti-inflammatory approved in the U.S., but it was too powerful to use more than twice in injection form. He could give me another shot, or he could write me a prescription for five days' worth; that would be all I'd ever get. I took the prescription, which I used only in emergencies, when there was something I absolutely had to do.

Dr. Mesipam also informed me that the CT scan showed I had something called sphenoid sinus disease, which was the cause of all the head pain I was experiencing. He explained that the sphenoid sinuses are small sinuses tucked between the eyes and the brain. They are completely landlocked, unlike our other sinuses. *Had all the smoke and ash set this off?* Possibly.

For the next several months, life was pretty challenging. A head that is constantly on the verge of exploding can really hinder normal living. Every toxin that surrounds us in our daily lives now became my enemy.

Fumes from diesel trucks and smoke were two of the worst culprits. A mere whiff of cleaning products took the top of my head off. Same with perfume. Cigar smoke made my entire head throb and made me sick to my stomach. Smelling paint fumes, fertilizers, gasoline, and any other chemical product made me feel like I'd been hit in the face with a frying pan.

Meanwhile, the fire was still going gangbusters, charring the mountains and valleys with unstoppable force. The ash we had to wade through when we climbed the stairs to our condo was like poison to me.

It wasn't until the end of October that the fire was finally declared controlled, after burning over 240,000 acres (almost a thousand square miles) and costing $117 million dollars to battle. It was a miracle that the only structures destroyed were two out buildings and a ranger station.

The fire we thought would never end did us the great favor of skirting all the homes and ranches it could've consumed in a blink of an eye. And at least it was finally over. But what I took away from our brush with the fire was a problem I could barely cope with. Added to what I already had to deal with, it just about pushed me over the edge.

On my next visit to Palo Alto, I discussed this new wrinkle with Dr. Q. His take on my sinus problem was a little different; as Lyme can go anywhere in the body, it was likely this new symptom was just another manifestation of the disease; the antimicrobials had it on the run and the sphenoid sinuses were a safe haven.

He gave me a small bottle of nasal drops manufactured in Germany, which cost $25 and only lasted a few days. As soon as I got back to Santa Barbara, I had to order more. After finishing the second bottle, I figured out whatever I was sticking up my nose wasn't working.

From about September to November, I had been experiencing a worsening of the Herxheimer's reaction. I had this gut feeling the doses I was taking of the two antimicrobials were too strong for my body to handle. I told Dr. Q my concerns several times, but he insisted I stay at the 45 drops per dose.

I knew after talking with others on the protocol that their doses topped out at 30 drops. With everything worsening after the brief period of improvement and the doctor not giving my complaints any credence, I decided—after eleven months on this regimen—I was through with this strategy. I felt things were headed the wrong direction. I concluded I was better off listening to what my body was telling me. After all, I knew me better than he did. And I was the one suffering.

In November, after abandoning the alternative approach, I realized I had to see what, if anything, the normal medical channels could do about the sphenoid sinus disease. I made an appointment with Dr. U, an ear, nose, throat specialist.

Dr. U was able to pull up the scans taken at the hospital on his laptop. He showed me the thickening of the membrane in the sphenoid sinuses. It was hard to imagine that such a minor physiological change could have such an enormous impact.

Dr. U told me the most effective way to treat this condition was to perform a surgery where he would run a tiny camera and a tiny drill up through my nose, behind my eyes to the sphenoid sinuses. He would then drill a hole in each sinus and, with a scalpel, cut away the offending tissue.

He had to admit there was some risk involved: blindness, brain damage and death were possible complications. I stared at him in disbelief. *Was that the only way to deal with this problem?* No. He would start me on a month's worth of antibiotics to see if this would clear up the problem and we would take it from there.

A month later, I was back in his office. The drugs hadn't helped. I was so desperate at this point, I wanted to have the surgery right then and there. But no such luck; in order for insurance to cover the procedure, I'd have to take antibiotics for another four weeks.

I took the second course with no improvement. Even though I was terrified of the procedure, I knew I couldn't live like this much longer. Something had to give. If surgery was my only option, that's what I would have to do.

Party Time

It was not the most wonderful time to be planning a party, but I didn't see any way to postpone turning fifty. Sure, I could've ignored it, or laid low and let it go by without any fanfare, but that would've fallen into the category of giving in to Lyme. Guy broached the subject a few months in advance of me turning the Big 5-0.

For years, it had been my hope to go to Ireland for my 50th. We know some folks there, relatives of close friends of ours who come to Santa Barbara every year. I had never been there, but it sounded like so much fun.

But now that my big day was on the horizon, all I wanted was to have my family around me: my sister and her son, my brother and his wife, my mother and my husband. Guy had the idea of us all going up to San Francisco for a long weekend celebration. I liked the sound of that a lot, but as we started to consider the logistics (especially where my mother was concerned), it started to feel too cumbersome. I wasn't even sure I could make the trip.

I left the idea alone for a while; it was hard enough getting through the days without the prospect of turning FIFTY looming over me. *Fifty? How did I get here so fast?* Last thing I remember was the surprise party Guy threw for my 40th, and the trip we took afterward to San Miguel de Allende and New Orleans.

It was shortly after I turned that ripe old age all my problems began. *Now I was turning 50?* My entire 40s had been spent trying to run to ground a disease I had just recently learned the name of. *Now I was about to enter hagdom?* It just wasn't fair. I had to fight back. I had to party down.

Though it was during one of my lowest points, the time had come for us to make arrangements. Party arrangements, not funeral. Since trying to convene in SF was not really a good option, I started considering what I would truly enjoy that I could physically handle.

I asked Guy if Summerland was booked during my birthday. It wasn't, so he said he'd block it out. Perfect; we'd throw a small party, no more than about 20 people, and have it catered. We'd move into the house a few days before hand to get everything ready.

My family—minus my mother, who already lived in Santa Barbara—would stay in the guest rooms. That's what I wanted. It would be easy for me; I could go lay down any time I wanted, and someone else would take care of all the cooking and cleaning. All I had to do was brace myself, then go straight into denial. If I didn't look fifty, then I wasn't really that old. Right?

About two months before the big day, we sat down with the owner of one of my favorite restaurants, Milk & Honey. Al met with us at our office and we put together a great menu, taken mostly from what he offered at his restaurant. We met at the Summerland house between tenants so Al could get the lay of our kitchen and the serve ware, since everything would be prepared at the house.

Setting the ball in motion put me in the proper spirit. I had gotten over the fifty thing once it occurred to me I was lucky to still be standing. Lyme had been kicking the crap out of me for a decade, and there were times when I didn't think I could persevere much longer. Making it to fifty was an achievement, one that I needed to commemorate.

One thing I had learned in the past several years was if you are planning a special event and you want to create a special playlist, you'd better get on it early. I'd been to three weddings where the music was relegated to the bottom of the list, and in all three cases, the couples regretted it and had to make do with whatever they could scrounge up at the last minute.

I learned my lesson vicariously and spent hours up at Woodstock compiling my list. I picked songs that were current favorites and mixed in songs that had made a mark on me throughout my life. It was a nice way for me to look back over the years, and it gave me a sense of comfort during a trying time.

Now everything was in place. No big sweat. I was in pretty bad shape physically, but I knew I would rally when the time came. My family was set to come down a few days prior to my birthday, which was on a Saturday.

But the Good Ship Birthday Party hit the rocks when I discovered that Guy had taken a booking up to the Friday before. I was devastated. My family was arriving on Tuesday. They were all supposed to stay with us. It was way too much work to try and move in at 3 p.m. on Friday and have everything in place for a party the next day. Besides, where was everyone going to stay until then? I was inconsolable.

It was Leah who came to the rescue. I was so upset, I was just going to call the whole thing off. She went online and found a really cute vacation rental on the Riviera for three nights. It took a bit of convincing on her part; I was over it by then. But Guy, who felt terrible about the situation, was willing to pay for the rental. Everyone was okay with that arrangement, so the party was back on.

The day I rolled over the odometer, I was barely functional. The spirit was all set to boogie down; the body, however, was ready for a quick trip to the morgue. I managed to assemble all the dinnerware, serving dishes, glasses and linens, then Mel and I went to lunch, mainly to get out of the caterers' way.

I had it in my head that I wanted to take a walk, but I was barely able to go 10 minutes before we had to turn around. Once we got back to the house, Mel spent almost three hours doing cranial-sacral work to get me up and running again.

Fortunately, it did the trick. I pulled it together and got myself ready. I had Brad snag me a plate of food, because I knew I wouldn't be eating once everyone arrived. I was shoveling it down when Brad brought in a gift from my mother, who had made herself sick so she wouldn't have to attend.

I realize that sounds awful, but it's the truth. A week before my birthday, my mother worked herself up in such a state of anxiety about coming to celebrate this milestone with me, she made herself ill. When I caught onto what she was doing, I took pity on her and let her off the hook. I didn't want her there at the expense of her health.

But it didn't make any difference. Her three children and only grandchild were all in town together, yet she clung to her story in order to avoid having to join us for anything. She told us she was unable to eat. It made me sad that she was so fearful of spending time with us that she went to such lengths to avoid it. Amazingly, the day after the party, she went out to lunch with Brad and Alice. She was in good spirits and had a very hearty appetite.

When Brad gave me the gift, he told me I needed to open it right away. He wanted to get my mom on the phone so I could thank her before the guests arrived. I wasn't thrilled with the arrangement, especially considering I was running behind in my transformation from sick, dead thing to party girl.

But it was obviously important to Brad, so I humored him. I obediently read the nice card and opened the box. Inside a small porcelain box was one of my mother's wedding rings. I didn't know how to react.

Why was she giving this to me? I wondered. But then it became obvious: she had given me the last of her finest possessions. She felt badly that she couldn't give of herself, so she gave me a diamond ring I didn't want or need. It was a flawless stone, which should've made it more special.

I have always taken the high road where my mother is concerned, yet I have to admit I felt very irked that she could commandeer my special day by ambushing me from the safety of her home. There may be some deeper, sadder interpretation of her actions, but on the level we dealt with one another, it felt like a grandstand play designed to make me feel guilty somehow.

I took the phone from Brad and thanked my mother for the ring. I told her I thought she should keep it—she might need it someday. No, no—she wanted me to have it. Okay, thank you. It's a perfect diamond, she reminded me. I know...it looks like you sent the appraisal along with it. Well, thanks Mom...that was very...nice of you...

That brief episode put a damper on my mood. The whole thing was just odd. I went back into my bedroom to finish dressing, trying to dispel the funky feeling that had settled over me. I was putting on the beautiful earrings Guy had given me for my birthday when I heard a faint knock on the door.

Out in the hallway stood Josiah, fresh from the hospital with the three steel plates in his arm; Justine, 8 months pregnant, and supposedly too worn out to travel; and little Dashiell Diamond Hamilton, 16-months old. I couldn't believe my eyes.

Josiah had called earlier to say they weren't going to be able to make it after all; Justine just wasn't up to it. Good, I had told him. There was no reason for them to drive 200 miles from Palm Springs with a broken wrist and Justine about to burst, just for my birthday. It wasn't worth it. Yet, there they were.

"Dash wasn't going to miss his Grandma Mikie's 50th birthday for anything in the world," Justine said, as I gave her a hug. I was so touched that they went to such lengths to be with me. It almost made me cry.

Around 11:00, Justine went upstairs to lie down with Dash. Josiah took them back to the hotel at midnight. At 8 a.m. the next morning, Guy got a call from Josiah; Justine's water had broken at 4 a.m. Josiah had to pack up everything, including the Pack-n-Play, Justine and Dash with one arm, and drive the 200 miles back to the desert.

The contractions were five miles apart in Beaumont, but somehow he managed to get to their hospital in time. Little Milliana Moon was the extra-special birthday present, born just one day after her Grandma Mikie's' Big 5-0.

DESPERADO

Now that I'd given up on the only alternative approach to treating Lyme that I knew of, I was pretty much at loose ends. It had been almost a year since I had gotten my diagnosis, and I had nothing to show for all my money or efforts, except a new, debilitating symptom. The pressure was on now to get well.

Since I knew what was wrong with me, I needed to treat it and make it go away. Having failed the first go round and wasted all that time and resources, I felt more at sea than ever. The research discounting antibiotic treatment for late-stage Lyme continued to pile up; the new consensus was that they just weren't effective. So, where do I go now?

I knew I had to deal with the sinus problem or I was in danger of throwing myself under a train. But I had a plan. I'd have the surgery, awful as the post-op was (gauze up the nose and tape across the nostrils for 3–4 weeks), and then—hopefully—my eyesight and brain would still be intact and my head wouldn't feel like it was going to explode anymore. At least I had that part figured out.

But what was I going to do about Lyme Central? I was basically adrift after quitting Dr. Q. I didn't have information on other methods, if there were any. I guess you could say I was "open to suggestions," which is another way of saying I was completely rudderless.

At our friend Dee's party, I was talking to a woman who told me of a doctor she had heard lecture. He had some innovative ways of dealing with diseases, mainly cancer, but she found his ideas quite intriguing. *Did he treat Lyme?* She didn't know, but said it might be worth checking out his clinic. She also told me he used hyperbaric oxygen chambers, which were touted to have all kinds of health benefits.

After doing a little online research, hyperbaric oxygen treatments sounded like they might do me some good. I called the clinic to get some information. I was quoted a price of $250 per hour-long session. That was enough for me to want to terminate the call.

But the girl on the other end of the line began questioning me about my situation, and before long, she had convinced me it would be a good idea to at least make an appointment with the director of the clinic to see if those treatments would be effective for me.

I had checked out the doctor online and his credentials were in good standing. I can't remember what the consultation cost, but I was sufficiently enticed to schedule a visit. I was still leery and a bit reluctant, but I didn't have a line on anything else, so I went for it.

I sat in the waiting area long enough to take in my surroundings. There was a bust of Dr. V's father sitting on a nearby table. Aside from this nod to the past, the office setup was a mix of alternative and traditional, which gave me hope that there was a middle ground between the two ideologies.

Over to my right was a large room filled with big, comfy-looking reclining chairs. There were several people sitting in the room with IV's in their arms. I knew that Dr. V's emphasis was on treating cancer patients through nutrition. Other than that, I didn't know much about the man I was there to see.

When at last he emerged, I was relieved to find that Dr. V seemed to be a man at ease in his environment. As confidence can be contagious, my spirits perked up a notch. I was still apprehensive, as part of me was suspect of every doctor I now came across, regardless of their ilk.

He motioned for me to follow him back to his private office, where we took our respective seats. Now it was time to perform, to make a case for myself and my odd collection of problems, which I could now present under the banner of Lyme disease. At least I had the credibility of having an established diagnosis. It sure made it easier to get to the point.

As I would find with other doctors who work from the fringes of accepted medicine, Dr. V wanted to hear the specifics. He wanted to look behind the handy diagnosis and judge my symptoms with his own diagnostic tools.

After giving him the rundown, he had me take a seat near a computer monitor while he placed electrodes on my thumbs. With a stylus that put out an electric charge, he would tap one of my fingers. The computer would register these responses with a range of beeps, and each reading was posted on the computer screen. In this manner, he checked me for a plethora of allergies and ailments.

After an exhaustive battery of testing, the program printed a list of all the things my body "had trouble with," which was a more modernized version of Dr. Q's approach. When we were finished, he explained what the program had detected: the main causes of my ailments—according to his findings—were spider venom and botulinum toxin, aka botulism.

Botulism? Really? How could I have gotten that? Dented food cans, honey, Dr. V speculated. I wasn't so sure about that. I'd had some very nasty spider bites, but wasn't *Borrelia Burgdorferi* at the root of my problems? Weren't Lyme spirochetes the cause of all my woes? Dr. V shrugged doubtfully and pointed to his results, as though this were the last word on the subject.

As we discussed his diagnosis, a machine created an antidote to counteract the poisons in my system. Just like that... *Presto, Magico*—a small glass bottle was filled. The same wizardry printed a label with my name, the date and the "cure." I was to take these drops until they were gone. Then I would be all well. *Oh really?*

As the jovial doctor escorted me out of his office, I got around to the reason behind my visit. *Would hyperbaric treatments help me with the pain?* Oh, absolutely! But I would need five. My head whipsawed on my neck. *Five sessions at $250 bucks a piece—that was $1,250. Okay, forget that.* Would I like to schedule my first one? *No,* I replied. *That's more than I could afford.*

"What do we charge for them?" he asked. I shrugged, not wanting to utter that number. He left the room to confer with someone. Upon returning, he asked if I could afford to pay $500 for a series of five. That was the equivalent of getting three free. Never one to pass up a deep discount, I said I could manage that.

Bargain made, Dr. V presented me at the reception desk and told his employee of our arrangement. I paid for the office visit and the $500 in advance, which made me a little nervous. I set up five appointments and went back to the office to mull over what I had signed onto this time.

On my second visit, I saw Dr. V for a follow-up prior to the hyperbaric treatment. How was I doing? Was I feeling better? I told him I hadn't seen any changes yet. He read through my file and whipped up another concoction for me to take.

He also gave me a homework assignment: I was to write a letter, a letter from the Lyme disease to me. Okay, I like writing and I have plenty of imagination—that was no problem. But what was I supposed to get from this exercise? Dr. V favored me with a cryptic smile.

One of the many staff members showed me into the room containing two hyperbaric oxygen chambers, which looked like giant white duffle bags. The woman unzipped the one not in use and explained how I was to climb in and lie down. Once settled, she would zip the top back up and turn on the oxygen valve.

I was to lay in there for an hour, during which time someone would come and check on me periodically. There was a clear panel of plastic above my eyes; I wouldn't be able to hear anyone very well because of the oxygen intake, but I could signal if I was okay or needed any assistance. Would I be all right?

I lay down, checking the degree of claustrophobia. It was similar in some ways to being trapped in an MRI machine, but roomier. At least I wouldn't be subjected to constant drumming. *Yes, I was going to be okay.*

Once the escape hatch was completely zipped closed and the hiss of the gas filled my ears, I did have a few moths flit around my insides. But I was relatively comfortable and grateful I had brought a security blanket—a cashmere shawl—as the pure air was a little chilly. I got so comfortable I almost nodded off. When I jerked back to alertness, I experienced a small burst of panic, which required reassuring myself that I was okay.

Other than those little jolts, the only problem I had with the experience was boredom. It was hard to lie there, doing nothing for an hour. Especially when I had so much work waiting for me back at the office. But once I crawled out of the duffle bag, I did feel different. A little lightheaded, a little giddy and wobbly. And I have to say that with each treatment, I did find I had more energy and less pain.

Back up at Woodstock, I tackled my writing assignment. I guess because it reminded me of homework, I wrote out this epistle from my Lyme nemesis on lined paper instead of using my computer. I felt a bit foolish, but I suppose there was no limit to the lengths I would go for the sake of getting well.

On my next appointment, I handed it in to Dr. V like a good girl, though I felt like an even bigger fool having done so. He barely glanced at it and I was relieved. I suppose there was a useful purpose to the exercise; if nothing else, it made me realize how hard I worked myself and how I essentially stacked the deck against beating the disease.

Had I acted on this insight and lightened my load, I may have enjoyed a real respite from pain after the five hyperbaric treatments. I actually did feel better, but that brief decrease in pain was stymied by the additional demands I put on myself.

It was now late December, and we decided to throw a small Christmas party. I was feeling pretty good; I could do it. It would be fun. We'd make a bunch of yummy food, make the house look festive. Nothing to it. Of course, we'd need to buy some gifts. And it would mean a fair amount of work, cooking for that many people. I'd have to swing by the Summerland house and pick up some serving platters and bowls and a few odds and ends. But it'd all work out.

It wasn't any surprise to me that pushing myself took its toll. The improvement I had seen from the treatments at Dr. V's clinic soon vanished. It wasn't realistic to think I'd change fifty years of behavior overnight. I never could sit still and my mind was always churning with tasks I wanted to complete. I'm just a doer, always have been. I enjoy doing, and I enjoy making things. And I hadn't really learned my lesson.

I was still of the opinion I should snap suddenly back to my former fitness and vigor without missing a beat. It was basically a contest of wills—Lyme against me. I was far too hardheaded to accept that I couldn't get well on my own terms. It would take me *years* to figure that one out, and even then I would be reluctant to embrace the art of doing less.

New Year, New Story, Old Saga

As we were going to be up at Woodstock for the holidays, we decided it would be a good time to have some friends up to stay. We hadn't been able to do that for a while and we both felt like we were missing out on the benefits of having a special retreat we could share with others.

Luckily, our good friends Chuck and Tawny were able to come up for the weekend. We always had a lot of fun when they came up and they were easy keepers. Whenever we all got together, we'd indulge in our favorite pastimes: hiking, eating, drinking, chatting away about books, music, movies, and the latest gossip.

Before they drove back to Santa Barbara, the four of us took a walk. Tawny and I fell behind and let Guy and Chuck choose the route. We meandered up and down and around, though Tawny and I barely noticed where we were going. We were much more interested in each other's stories than where the men took us. But I remember very clearly when and where the inspiration for my next book hit me.

We had looped around and were heading up Woodstock Road toward our front gate. As Tawny was telling me about the latest antics of mutual acquaintances, both of whom were in the real estate business, all the stories I had heard over the years from Guy and others came together in my mind. I realized at that moment I had a wealth of humorous material based on first hand experiences and second-hand accounts to fill a book.

All those anecdotes merged, and in one momentary flash, I saw the entire book play out in my mind's eye. I saw the thirty-something grocery clerk, bored out of her mind, desperate for release from the job she had grown to despise, longing for a career that could provide a real future for her and her son. I saw an empty-headed realtor—short on sense and long on enthusiasm—handing out cards in Roxanne's checkout line.

As Tawny told her stories, the pieces continued to fall into place. By the time we got back to the house, my mind was spinning.

With the new year coming, I had been thinking about re-editing *Alligators* to get it ready for submission. Editing required a lot less typing, and it seemed like a good way to ease back into writing after an eight-month abstinence. I would be able to see how much my body could take, see how my back and fingers held up under light duty.

But once this new idea popped into my brain, nothing could stop me. I had a story and I had to get it written, no matter what my body had to say about it.

I started *Golden State* in the first week of 2008. The protagonist, Roxanne Platt, is a single mom who's been working as a checker at the ValuWise grocery store for thirteen long, boring years. During that time she has seen a parade of managers, but none as tyrannical as Stan Kemplehoff, her current tormenter-in-chief.

Stan's micro-managing, bullying ways have driven Roxanne to reassess her life, an examination that leaves her feeling hopeless and irritable. As she scours the Classifieds for alternative employment, she recalls a real estate agent who had been in her checkout line, and wonders why she couldn't enjoy the same success as Lois Bronsen—*top 2% in the state.*

***

Starting a new project was a great tonic for me. Nothing had changed on the Lyme front, but I once again had my writing to keep my spirits up and keep me sane. It was the secret would I could escape to a few hours a week, and it was the one thing that gave me hope Lyme wouldn't completely strip me of my identity.

The thrill of having a new book to work on distracted me for a few weeks, but then it became mandatory that I deal with the sphenoid thing. It had become impossible to keep up the pretense of a normal existence when so many things in our daily environment set off crushing pain episodes.

For months, I could barely function. I did, but not as anything human. It was as if my head were encased in iron, the heavy metal squeezing against the bones in my face and skull, crushing it, making even the slightest movement excruciating. Getting back into writing again was important on so many levels; getting the sinus problem fixed was essential.

I went back to see Dr. U. Since I had completed the two courses of antibiotics, he was able to get the green light from the insurance company to perform the surgery. He examined the area again and explained the procedure in detail.

As badly as I wanted this agony to end, I have to admit I had real trepidation about having a tiny camera and drill and scalpel travelling up my nose, hopefully bypassing my eyes and my brain. When I brought up the fact that I had a deviated septum, Dr. U said he could try to repair it on the way out. This was a bonus; I might be able to get rid of the whistling in my nose that sometimes kept me awake at night.

I mentioned my left nostril was smaller than the right and therefore clogged up worse. I told him about the torticollis I'd had at birth, which causes facial asymmetry. I'd had treatments for the first 18 months, but I still had some asymmetry to my features.

Dr. U regarded me and said, "Oh, I see that." The fact that he hadn't picked up on this from the start made me nervous. I left wondering if he would remember this quirk while he was going about the business of shoving apparati up my nose. Given the number of surgeries he performed, I was doubtful. Forgetting my quirks might throw his calculations off, which in turn could cause some serious problems. I felt even more nervous than before.

In order to undergo this surgery, I would first need to have a full physical. I scheduled the appointment with Dr. Mesipam. I then tried to psyche myself up for the procedure. But in the time between both appointments, Fate stepped in and dislodged one of my crowns. Fortunately, I didn't swallow it. Instead, I was able to take it to my dentist, Dr. R, and have it put back on.

After Dr. R reattached my crown, I went up to the front desk to pay for the charges. Barbara, his office manager, told me I hadn't been in for a teeth cleaning in almost two years. She tried to get me to schedule an appointment, but I told her I was about to have surgery and the recovery time would be long. When she found out what the surgery was for, she smiled tersely. She knew all about sphenoid sinus disease; she'd had the surgery and her problems got worse. This was not the kind of news I wanted to hear.

Barbara asked if I'd ever taken any Chinese herbs. I had years ago, but not for sinus problems. Barbara handed me a brochure of an acupuncturist, who happened to be Dr. R's wife. Barbara told me she had been about to have a second surgery when Julie suggested she try two Chinese remedies. Within a week, Barbara was feeling better. Within two weeks, her symptoms were completely gone.

I called and left a detailed message for Julie as soon as I got back to the office. When she returned my call, I explained that I had a surgery scheduled in less than three weeks. She was able to work me in three times a week in hopes of seeing improvement before then.

In the meantime, I went to see Dr. Mesipam to have the physical. I told him the pain from the sphenoid sinus disease had gotten unbearable. He sympathized; he had other patients with the same condition. When he asked if he could make a suggestion, I was very receptive.

"Don't do it," he said simply. I was not expecting this. "I've seen too many people worse off after the surgery." *Worse?* I still couldn't fathom such a thing. It didn't take any further coaxing to change my mind. He gave me a nasal spray he said might help relieve the symptoms. He also thought the acupuncture might be worth a try. I took the spray and his advice. I called to cancel the surgery as soon as I got back to my car.

I was very relieved by the turn of events. Once I called it off, I breathed easier. Anything could've gone wrong. Even if it hadn't, I could've gone through the surgery and the agonizing month-long recovery and not seen any improvement. With that behind me now, I concentrated my hopes on getting better with the Chinese approach.

The nice thing about seeing an acupuncturist is that it's like one-stop shopping. I asked Julie if she could treat the Lyme along with the sinus issue. She did some research and put me on a few different Chinese remedies. I continued seeing her three times a week for a few months. I had two major obstacles to overcome; I knew that couldn't happen overnight. I could be patient. It was my only hope.

GAME CHANGER

While I was running from doctor to doctor, Guy was busy reading the tea leaves. It was March of 2008, and the economy was on shaky ground. We had seen the bellwethers of the coming mortgage crisis when the industry leaders were swallowed by their competitors, starting in late 2007. The resulting consolidation brought about big changes to the way lenders did business.

Guy was not at all comfortable about what he saw coming. We were at the tip of the foreclosure fiasco, and though we had never as a company been involved in risky loans, the new regulations coming from the federal government were going to have a significant impact on all brokers.

Over the twenty-three years Guy had operated our mortgage company, he was often courted by the large lending institutions to come work for them. For the first time, he was seriously entertaining their offers. By March, he started negotiations with a direct lender. If he was going to make a move like that, leave his own mortgage company, he was going to need certain guarantees. And Leah would have to be part of deal.

Meanwhile, life for me was pretty much the same as usual. Except that an ugly problem was about to reappear in the most gruesome possible way.

After a morning of working at my desk, I went to the store to buy food for lunch and the weekend migration to Woodstock. I was on the freeway when I heard a loud *THUNK!* Immediately, the air conditioner stopped working. *Oh, great,* I thought. We'd have to drive over the Pass without any air.

Fortunately, I had already made an appointment to take the Jeep to the mechanic in Los Olivos on Friday. When I got back to the office, I called to make sure they'd have enough time to take a look at the A/C.

Because the apartment was downtown and close to everything, neither of us drove the car until Thursday afternoon when it was time to head up to the ranch. We packed the car with the food, cat, computers and hopped in. As soon as Guy turned the key in the ignition, we were blasted in the face with the horrendous odor of decomposing rodent.

We rolled down all the windows and closed all the vents while we sputtered and gagged. *Holy shit!* That's what made the air conditioning stop working. This was unbelievable. This was a nightmare. There was nothing we could do but drive up to the ranch with all the windows down, heat and fumes blasting us in the face, along with vapors of dead mouse.

From the first instant the stench hit my nostrils, my sphenoid sinuses signaled a full-scale offensive. Every square inch of my face and head throbbed mercilessly. The tissue I held to my nose was pitiful defense against the stomach-turning odor that permeated the car.

The next morning when we took the Jeep in to the shop, I had to drive Guy's truck, while he got stuck driving the mouse mobile. I watched from the safety of the Ford as Guy explained the situation to Ken, the manager.

Hands went to noses immediately whenever someone got within five feet of the vehicle. It was obvious that they were as unhappy with this surprise as we were, maybe more so. When Guy got in the truck he said they almost turned him away. Cringe. We felt terrible, but what could we do? Neither one of us knew the first thing about auto mechanics, and we sure the heck didn't know how to dismantle the air conditioning system.

We waited nervously for the call from Ken telling us the car was ready. When Ken finally called, he was not in a good mood. Guy dropped me off and let me handle it from there. Gone were the happy smiles I usually generated when I walked into Los Olivos Motors.

Ken, an Englishman with impeccable manners, had no problem telling me how awful the whole day had been—having to dive in under the hood and work without breathing while they took the A/C apart, finding the decapitated mouse and having to dispose of it, pouring bottles of deodorizer into the system and trying to flush out the putrid air.

I stood there letting him vent in his soft-spoken manner, humbly submitting myself to his justifiable rant as I offered an unbroken stream of apologies. *We're so sorry...we didn't know about this until the drive up yesterday evening...we didn't know what else to do... we're sorry... thank you for taking care of it, thank you, thank you....*

Even though he was understandably ticked off at us, he did order mesh screening that he would later use to construct a mouse-proof barrier between the engine and the interior of the car. Episodes like this should never happen again.

I drove back to the ranch with the windows down, barely risking a breath. I couldn't decide which was worse—the traces of dead rodent or the derodorizer.

I felt humiliated, of course, but I also felt whipped, as though life was giving me the booby prize for some failure on my part. I guess I just felt like I could never win against forces that could invade your car with vermin. Had I known then what else was in store for me, I would've pushed the car over a cliff and walked home. On second thought, maybe home would've been the wrong direction.

Unfortunately for us, this nasty incident was the start of a long war of man against nature. Where we lived in Woodstock was by any account a rural area. When you are out as far as we were, you have to take the pluses with the minuses of communing with nature.

We were regularly treated to spectacular sights: deer crisscrossing our property along the game trails, drawn to our house by the music playing on the Bose; waking up at dawn to two great-horned owls outside our bathroom window, one taking up the entire bird bath, the other on the tree limb above; dozens of beautiful birds that constantly frolicked all around the house.

Equally thrilling, though ominous, was watching the bobcats, mountain lions, coyotes, and the occasional fox cruising past our windows. The not-so-nice wildlife we encountered included snakes, badgers, skunks, raccoons, wild pigs, ground squirrels and field mice. The smallest of these creatures had the biggest impact on us.

It had been a year since we had driven to Santa Barbara with four mice in our company. After the decapitated mouse in the A/C episode, the flood gates seemed to open. For whatever reason, (heavy rains leading to a mouse population explosion?) mice had suddenly, after six years, decided living in a Jeep was preferable to living in the wild.

Going out to my car became risky business; I had to cautiously investigate from one end to the other looking for evidence that any four-legged monsters had broken in since I last looked.

When this nightmare first started, Guy and I tore the car apart trying to figure out why all of the sudden they were getting in. We soon found the lure: the stash of almonds and pumpkin seeds I kept there. We now found these treats cached all over the vehicle: under the seats, in the spare tire cover, in all the pockets.

We vacuumed and disinfected every inch of the car, only to repeat the process every week. I no longer kept food in the car, but it didn't matter; the word was out and the Jeep had become *the* destination for every hip mouse within a mile of our house.

After we first discovered this new wave of invaders, we placed sticky traps in the car at night, and checked them every morning while we were up at the ranch. The drill was to arm myself with gloves and a garbage bag. If nothing needed to be taken to the morgue (trash can), I would continue the search for the telltale signs of mouse activity.

As the weeks and months went on, the number of incidents rose. We had engaged an exterminating service after the onset, and our guy, Daniel, made weekly trips to our property in an effort to bring this mouse business to a close.

As bad and confounding as the B&E of our car had been, the real affront started when they moved their operations to the house. Now we had sticky traps everywhere, plus an inordinate number of bait stations. We had experts from the "home office" come to sleuth and problem solve.

Every *Aha!* moment failed to yield the hoped-for results. We routinely had two or more experts crawling the house from top to bottom. They were confident they would stop the problem in the house; we were out of luck as far as the car was concerned.

As you can imagine, a good deal of my waking time was spent contemplating this mess. Almost anyone who knows me will tell you I'm something of a clean freak. This situation was a gross-out with psychological impact. I was mortified on every level.

And let's face it, mouse droppings are not the kind of thing you want to be in contact with when combating an illness. To say that I was freaked out is an understatement. But what could I do? If there were dead mice or droppings, they had to be cleaned up. I soldiered on, fighting a war I had begun to fear I'd never win.

What had me the most puzzled—besides their point of entry—was how these new mice had the instinct to poke around until they found a small breach in the exterior of our car when there were no longer any treats waiting for them. The mice that could've passed on this knowledge had become part of a landfill.

Weirder still, after months of catching mice in traps, a diabolical change occurred: mice were still entering the vehicle, only now they managed to avoid the sticky traps that virtually carpeted the floor space.

Meanwhile, back in the house, the mouse drama had reached a fevered pitch. The incident that stands out most prominently in my mind happened when we got up to the ranch late one Thursday.

It had been a very hectic day at the office and Guy and I were mentally thrashed. I hadn't even had a chance to lie down all day and was in a lot of pain. But once we got to the house, there were all the usual chores to deal with.

Around 7:30, when I was finally able to lie down for a few minutes, I was beyond beat. I reached over to my bedside table for a tissue. Even in my exhausted state, I knew that tissue boxes aren't supposed to rattle. I jumped up and ran the box into the family room where Guy was watching the news.

"There's something rattling around in there—I can't look," I said, thrusting the box at him. Cautiously, he lifted the lid and took the tissue box out of the cover. We both peered inside. Down at the bottom was this small, granular stuff, like sand.

There was something familiar about the color that jogged my memory. It looked like the new cat litter I had started buying—some natural thing, supposed to be healthier for cats, made out of...*corn*. Holy crap! I had inadvertently offered up the world's largest mouse buffet.

I looked around. I grabbed the tissue box in the family room and shook it. *Rattle, rattle, rattle.* Around the house I went, making sickening discoveries in every room.

As I passed through the kitchen, I noticed the cat staring intently at his dome-covered, corn-filled cat box. Even though he's not much of a mouser, he is a pretty reliable pointer. Sure enough, a mouse skittered across the floor, disappearing under the living room sofa.

Now, I can cope with dead mice, though I'm hardly sanguine about it. But live, running mice make me scream like an eleven-year-old girl. Brooms came out, and so did the sticky traps. Ironically, we had become so confident that the exterminators had gotten the indoor mouse problem under control, we no longer had traps all over the floor.

After a few ineffectual efforts at dislodging the mouse, Guy gave up and started making dinner. It was now about 8:00. As I walked back into our bedroom, I saw the cat staring at the bedside table. As I informed Guy of this new worry, a mouse darted passed me into the kitchen. *Two mice! Unbelievable!*

By now I needed some drugs, preferably sedatives. I had nothing, so I lay back down, keeping one eye on the kitchen floor, which I had a good view of from my perch. When Guy went into the family room for a moment, I detected movement out of the corner of my eye. I saw the cat nosing around the stove and I jumped up to investigate. Hallelujah! We caught one!

We were just disposing of that intruder when the cat came barreling through the kitchen, hot on the trail of another varmint. I followed the parade while Guy saved the dinner from burning up. The mouse the cat and I were after disappeared under our bed. Visions of awaking in the middle of the night to one of those things crawling up my leg almost made me wild with fear. *Go, cat, go—get that mouse! Don't just sit there!*

While I was standing an uneasy vigil at a safe distance from the bed, Guy spotted yet another mouse. This was starting to feel like something out of a Stephen King novel. I can't remember what my next move was, but I suspect I went to make myself a drink. I do remember more activity in the bedroom and seeing that mouse make a mad dash for the kitchen. By this time, dinner was ready.

I guess it says something about our shell-shocked mentality that we were able to go into the family room and eat, knowing we had a least two rodents on the loose in our house. The good news about this night is that when we finished eating we found two mice in separate traps. We went to bed after laying out every trap we had left, and thankfully they were all empty when we woke up the next day.

After the Three Mouse Night, I made a rather distraught call to the exterminators. This prompted more inspections and more brainstorming. Finally, they came up with another idea. They had already patched what few breaches they could find on the exterior of the house; the only possible way they could still be getting in was through some small, undetectable gap in the roof.

The solution: cut back the oak and pine tree limbs that hung close to the roof line and the trumpet vine on the lattice that shaded the east side of the house, the theory being that mice wanted in our house so badly, they would climb the trees and leap onto the roof and find some tiny gap, dislocate their miserable little shoulders and slither through.

Unconvinced but desperate, we had our gardener get on it immediately. I'm happy to report that no mouse ever entered our house again. Once we were sure—really, really sure—that it was all over, we had two cleaning companies come and demouse our house, cleaning every nook and cranny and all the carpets and upholstery. After a harrowing ordeal, we had our happy home back at last. The Jeep, unfortunately, was not so lucky.

One morning, Guy and I left separately to go back into town. I had made an appointment to take the cat to the vet, which was on the way to the office. I was feeling very organized that day; take cat in, do some work in the office, see the acupuncturist, then finally go to the chiropractor she had recommended. I knew my neck was out and I hadn't had any adjustments in about twenty years. I really needed to see someone.

Things were going pretty smoothly that morning. I remember it was a gorgeous August day. The cat and I had just left the vet and were heading down the freeway to the office. Suddenly, there was another horrible *THUD!*, followed by a sickening *thunk, thunk, thunk*. I just about had a heart attack. *Please, God—not this again!*

I rushed the kitty upstairs and immediately got on the phone to Ken. I told him what had happened. *I'm really sorry. I don't know what to do. But if I wait until Thursday...* Ken told me to come back up right after lunch. Julie was able to rearrange her schedule and got me in early. I lay there on her table doing my porcupine impersonation, thoroughly traumatized. *How could this possibly be happening again?*

When I got up to Los Olivos, Ken was waiting for me, bless his English soul. Without wasting a minute, he began accessing the A/C filter from the passenger's side. I felt so badly as I watched him struggle, his body half in, half out of the car. I don't know why he didn't tell me to go away and never come back the first time.

After half an hour of contortions, Ken removed the filter. We held our collective breath as he took the top off. He extended the filter toward me. I could barely look. There, caught in the folds, was a dead leaf. I didn't know whether I should laugh or cry. Ken looked the same way. He put everything back together, absolutely refused payment, and sent me on my way.

Even though it had been a false alarm, I was still feeling pretty rung out by the experience. I felt foolish, but then again, how could I have known? A thunk is a thunk. There was no way Los Olivos Motors would've removed another putrefying mouse carcass. We had gotten that message loud and clear.

So, I had done the right thing. I had screwed up my day and Ken's and caused myself a whole lot of stress I didn't need. But considering the circumstances, it could've been much worse.

As I drove back down the coast, I started deliberating whether I should stop at the chiropractor's or not. I'd be driving right by there. I felt horrible, but I knew I was in need of some serious bone cracking, which ultimately would make me feel better. I looked at the clock; almost 3:00. I steadied myself and decided to take the plunge. I'm so glad I did.

Dr. Johnson couldn't have been nicer. I told him my neck felt like it was out. I also told him I had congenital torticollis, which prompted him to do a series of X-rays. When he came back into the examining room with the developed films, he was quite excited. He had only seen one, maybe two cases of neck misalignment as bad as mine. He hung the X-rays on the light box and pointed out his discoveries. But not to worry; he could help me.

As he positioned me on the chair and started a physical examination of my neck and back, I thought I better let him know about the Lyme problem, too. He stopped what he was doing, scooted around to face me and said, "Girl, no!" It had been a while since I had talked to any new doctors about my diagnosis. Dr. Brad was a very sympathetic listener. It was nice to have someone show such concern.

Over the next few months, I went to see Dr. Brad two or three times a week. He was able to help me so much. It was bizarre to me that I had so much pain, I couldn't differentiate between the various causes. A healthy person would've been in to see someone years ago. Nonetheless, I was grateful Julie had pointed me in his direction. He was able to unkink my neck, as well as adjust my back, hips, shoulders, and wrists on a regular basis.

One morning after my adjustments, Dr. Brad casually asked what I was going to do that day. I told him I was going to go buy a new car. After parking the Jeep in various spots around the property, it became obvious it couldn't go to the ranch anymore. There was some breach somewhere that was allowing mice to get in. It never happened to the truck, even though Guy kept horse biscuits in the ashtray.

There was a Jeep I had been stalking for a month. Right after the false alarm, I went online to see what was out there. Our other Jeep was old and had served us well; it wasn't its fault it had suddenly become irresistible to vermin.

When I had gone to test drive the one I ultimately purchased, I causally asked the salesman about the air-tightness of the vehicle. Could, for example, a *mouse* get in? I didn't sign the dotted line until I was absolutely convinced nothing like that would ever happen again. And thankfully, it didn't.

In June, Guy and Leah had gone to work for a direct lender. With them gone, I took care of closing the remaining loans in our pipeline. Once the last loan was audited and filed away, I started the process of shutting down our company. Our fiscal year-end was September 30th, which was perfect timing. By my birthday, my ten-year stint as accidental office manager was behind me. I was now happily unemployed.

With Guy and Leah out of the office, and all my official duties over, it felt strange to be in the office/apartment all day, just me and the cat. The apartment, which we created to simplify our lives when we had the mortgage company and lived up in the Valley, now didn't seem wholly justified. We still needed to be in Santa Barbara for Guy's work, but I wondered how long I would have to skulk around an empty office.

As fall approached, I suggested we move into Summerland for the week of Thanksgiving. We had blocked out that holiday after the first two years, when I realized what a beating the house took during the annual feeding frenzy. Guy was all for it.

I got very excited and spent a good deal of time at the house, sometimes with our handyman, Mike, trying to bring it back to its former condition. I bought some new things: rugs, towels, pillows, new fabric for the dining chairs, bedspreads and sundry other items to help remove the thought of the hundreds of strangers who had streamed in and out of our house over the previous five years.

As we did every week of our lives, we packed up the food, computers, cat, plus some clothing and this time moved back into our own home for a week. As soon as we got there, Guy proposed we stay there an extra week. Why not? Now we were really excited.

As the days passed, it occurred to us we didn't actually need to leave until the 28th of December, when the next tenant arrived. Yippee! Now we were having fun. Even though we hadn't lived in the house for over five years, it felt like we'd never left. It was such a good feeling, being back in our home. Especially so for me; Summerland was all I ever needed.

In early December, I started concentrating on life simplification again. There was one property both of us would be glad to sell, and that was the Palm Springs rental, Casa Bonita—or as I fondly called it, Casa Bonehead Idea.

We had put CB on the market twice, but because it was a vacation rental and because Palm Springs is a seasonal resort town, our house was always listed when it was fully booked, which made showing it almost impossible. We actually had it in escrow twice, but it fell out both times.

I knew from checking the calendar that there was a three-week window before Christmas and New Year's when it was not booked. I did some heavy lobbying and finally convinced Guy the time was right: if I went down there and met with a painter and a handyman and the gardeners, I could whip the place back to its former glory and we could put it back on the market. He reluctantly agreed, and somehow I pulled together enough fortitude to drive down there and make everything happen.

It was a productive trip. The painter and I came to terms on the cost before I went down, so we did a walk-through to make sure we hadn't overlooked anything. Then I went through everything in the house that needed repairing or replacing with the handyman. From that day on, I was able to communicate with them by phone and email. A few glitches came up, the most expensive being replacement of the entry gate.

Three weeks later, Guy and I drove down and inspected the results. Everything looked better than when we initially furnished it. It had taken a lot more work than I had anticipated, and naturally more money, but I was so glad we had done it. Now *maybe* we could get it sold and have one less burden to worry about.

Our wonderful six-week stay in Summerland ended and it was time to go back to our old routine. We packed and I locked up some of the new things I didn't want anyone but us to use, not that I knew when we would ever have the chance to stay there again.

It was a few days before New Year's, so we went up to the ranch. It didn't take long before I was overcome with remorse. I was not happy with the prospect of picking up where we had left off: weekdays in the office, all alone, and weekend sprints up to the ranch. Cleaning both places before we left. Hauling groceries up to the apartment and then back down to the car.

What was my life now? I had no job, yet I lived part of the week in an office. Why couldn't I live in one house—*our house*—instead of this crazy arrangement that no longer suited me at all?

I was sick. I was on my last legs, and I knew it. I also knew that if I didn't make a change in my life, I was never going to get better. There were too many senseless responsibilities in my life. I needed to scale way back, or I wasn't going to last much longer.

After coming face to face with this realization, I put it straight to Guy: either we move back into Summerland, or... I didn't finish the sentence, but it was clear to me that by any means necessary, I had to change my life. I had to at least live like a normal person. If I kept going at this insane pace, it would surely kill me. I was making the choice to save my life. If Guy refused, I would've left, simple as that. I had finally had enough.

TRANSITION TIME

It was hard for Guy to give up renting out Summerland. During the five years it had served as a vacation rental, it generated a lot of income for us. It took him a while to accept what I was asking for. But when he realized how beaten down and close to despondency I was, he reluctantly agreed: he would take the property off the rental sites and tell all the unpaid prospects the house was no longer available.

We both felt it wouldn't be right to cancel those reservations that had been paid in full, even though it was still legally possible with two of them. There were three such commitments: one for the entire month of January; one in mid-March; and one in late April. This meant we would have to move in and out three more times before we could move back in for good.

So, in the meantime, life reverted back to the usual for the month of January. Guy would go to work Monday through Thursday and I would do my thing. Up to the ranch Thursday afternoons and back to the apartment on Monday morning.

Now that we were on a countdown, I was able to console myself that things would soon be much easier. I knew they would be harder in the short term, but it would be worth it in the end. I started thinking about what it would take to make the shift from the apartment/office to Summerland, and I kept working on *Golden State*.

On February 1st, our month-long tenants moved out. It was a Sunday. I had cleaned Woodstock and done all my other chores and had most of our things packed in the Jeep. I was trying to get as much work in on *Golden State* as I could before Guy got back from his ride.

By the time he returned and got cleaned up, I had finished the story. I had such a feeling of accomplishment. It had been years since I had completed a book, and I was relieved to find I still had it in me.

Over the next three months, we divided our time between the three places. It was extra hectic, but I couldn't have stayed in the apartment when Summerland wasn't rented. Those days were over. Summerland was our home again. Soon, anyway.

On April 30th, 2009, we packed up as much stuff out of the apartment as our vehicles could hold and made the ten-minute drive to Summerland. By this time, Guy was as excited as I was to be back home for good. With his new job, it was nice to come home to a real house. The apartment was great and really served its purpose while we had our business next door.

But now we didn't need the office condo at all. We listed it and waited for the right buyer.

I suppose I had this idea that once I moved back into Summerland and didn't have to clean up after strangers or shuttle back and forth between three properties, I would start to feel better. I was happier, for sure, but all my symptoms were still in high gear. Other than acupuncture and Chinese herbs, I wasn't doing anything to fight the Lyme.

My sister, always on the lookout for a cure, heard about a doctor near her who'd had great results treating Lyme disease, among other things. She knew from some of his patients that he used a dark field microscope to look at live blood, and from that he could determine which isopathics (super-homeopathics) to prescribe. Acting as a scout, she made an appointment to have her own blood examined.

While she was waiting to see Dr. W, another patient and her family were saying their goodbyes to the staff. It was a very emotional parting, with hugs and tears. After they left, the receptionist told Melanie that the girl, who was in her late teens and using a cane, had come to the clinic five months earlier in a wheelchair. Her mother had carried her in; she was not much more than skin and bones.

Over the previous twelve years, the family had been to every kind of doctor, tried every drug known to treat Lyme, and then some. Their first visit was a last-ditch effort to get her well. Now she was almost off all her pain medications, had gained weight and was functioning more or less like a normal teenager. It was nothing short of a miracle for her and her parents.

Dr. W took a slide of Melanie's blood and placed it under his microscope. Without asking a lot of questions, he was able to see she is in very good health. All the factors that he looked for were exactly as they should be, which was something he rarely saw.

Mel had a minor health concern, which he treated with injections in her tonsil pillars at the back of her mouth. But her primary reason for going to see him was to find out if he could help me. Dr. W told her about his approach to treating illnesses and injuries, and how he looked to the blood for clues on which areas of the body have blockages, what the Chinese call stagnant qi.

As a demonstration of his ability to target problem areas, which then allows the body to mend itself, he showed her a video of a former patient riding a bicycle. The woman, who had come to him in a wheelchair, had been paralyzed after being raped, thrown off a cliff and left for dead. It was amazing she had survived her ordeal, and even more amazing that she could walk again after other doctors had told her otherwise.

After hearing the account of the other Lyme patient and this woman, I was willing to give his methods a try. What did I have to lose? I had no other viable options. I called his office. Dr. W was booking three months out at the time, but he had a cancellation in mid-August. I took it.

The remodel at the office was completed right before my trip to Nevada City. I had planned to have the place professionally cleaned before we put it back on the market, but after making a walk-through, I didn't think it was necessary. That was a miscalculation on my part, but once I figured that out, I had already cleaned the worst of it and there really wasn't any need to hire someone.

In the end, it was definitely more than I should've been doing. It was a classic move for me, always pushing myself beyond my limits, only to pay for it later. I just couldn't get used to my physical limitations, even after all those years.

Three days before my trip north, I hit my lowest point. I'd had many "lowest points," but this particular plunge made it clear I had finally hit bottom. It was a day filled with so much pain, I could do little more than lie on the bed and cry.

I had been pretty stoic up until this point, with only occasional blubbering meltdowns. But unlike previous low points, as I lie there searching for one ray of hope, one thought that could give me comfort, I could find nothing. I could not stir a single emotion.

Thoughts of family, friends, former hopes, future hopes—nothing could raise a blip on the radar screen of my soul. There was absolutely nothing left inside me. I thought that if I had died right then and there, I would've felt no regrets in leaving this world behind. All my life amounted to at that point was an endless tide of pain. My body was nothing more than a hell suit. Shedding it would've been a huge relief.

The problem with being at the end of your resilience but not at the end of your life is that you must continue living. I didn't die that day. I couldn't even work up enough impetus to take my own life. It would've required more thought and strength than I could muster. I passed the night in a state of mental numbness.

When I woke, I was still in a lot of pain, but I could feel a thin hope rising in me: *if I can get there, they will take care of me.* This became my mantra over the next two days. All I had to do was get there; my sister and brother would take care of me after that. And hopefully this new doctor would have insights the others didn't.

On Monday morning, I got on the plane to Sacramento, where my brother picked me up. I had made it. I stayed at Mel's house and placed myself in her care. She was ready for me. She fed me, soaked and massaged my feet, did cranial sacral therapy on me.

We did as much as I could handle, and lay around the rest of the time, talking. That alone was enough to reboot my system; I no longer felt like the walking dead, but I was still pretty sketchy. A strong wind could've knocked me on my back.

My first appointment with Dr. W was on Thursday. As we pulled into the parking lot, Melanie advised me to "ham it up" when I got into the office.

"Why? Don't you think he'll believe me?" I asked, half-panicked. I hadn't prepared myself for another disbelieving doctor. I had automatically assumed from what I'd heard that this one would be more simpatico.

"Yeah, he will. But just ham it up," Mel insisted.

"The proof will be in the blood, won't it?"

"Yeah, but just ham it up a little." When I started to protest again, Mel cut me off. "Listen, you look like you're forty and you don't look sick."

Despite the coaching, I couldn't force myself to limp into the office. I *was* sick, and if this doctor couldn't detect that, well then I probably shouldn't be putting any hope in him. But now I was doubtful; what if this guy couldn't help me? What was I going to do then?

Dr. W was quick to get down to business. What little small talk there was he directed to Melanie. Once that was out of the way, he focused his attention on me.

"Okay, let's see what we've got here," he said, as he scooted over to me with a needle and a slide. He pricked my finger, wiped it with a tissue, squeezed another bead of blood out, which he wiped onto the slide. He set that slide down, then repeated the process with a second slide. He rolled back to his microscope and examined the drops of blood.

Immediately, he was intrigued. He switched on the monitor in front of me so I could see what he saw at 30,000-times magnification. Even though I was uninitiated in the examination of live blood, it seemed very chaotic-looking to me, sluggish and disorganized.

After switching the lenses and checking the perimeter of the smear and back to the other views, and making quiet remarks to himself as he did so, Dr. W suddenly swiveled back around. He looked at me as if seeing me for the first time.

"Your eyes don't line up," he said, pushing my hair back from my face. I explained that I had torticollis due to complication at birth. Dr. W became very excited, his eyes riveted on mine.

"Tell me everything about your birth," he said, as he slid his chair over to his computer. I told him I had been breach and at one point the doctor asked my father which one of us he should try to save, mother or child. There was a good deal of struggle getting me out, which resulted in my neck being torqued, which caused a type of paralysis.

Dr. W listened to this account with mounting excitement. He sat thoughtfully for a long moment while he assimilated the facts. He scooted directly in front of me and regarded me carefully.

"Your nervous system is fried and your adrenals are shot," he said matter-of-factly. "You look like a doll on the outside, but inside, you're a mess. You're barely functioning. I don't know how you're still going.

"There are three causes of death: cancer—which is a mold—circulatory, and arthritis. You are almost completely rigid with arthritis." Though these were harsh words, I knew they were true. Finally, someone was able to look at me and understand what I felt like on the inside.

"Should I go buy a coffin?" I asked. Dr. W laughed.

"No. We're going to try to make you better," he said, patting me on the knee. He drew our attention back to the blood.

"See these cells here? See how they overlap? See how misshapen they are? See all this grey, grainy stuff in the background? It's not supposed to look like this. All these cells here—see how they're hollowed out? Those are dead. Your blood cells are dying at an alarming rate."

"What are those big, bright things?" I asked, pointing to a large, crystal-like formation.

"That one is your brain." Dr. W moved the lens around the slide. "That's a giant megakaryocyte. That's your sinuses." Mel and I looked at each other. This was encouraging; the sphenoid sinus disease was a major problem for me. Maybe there *was* something to all this weird science.

"Have you ever had any sinus trauma...broken nose?" I told him about the nose bleeds I'd had since I was very young, and the three subsequent nasal cauteries, starting when I was twelve. Dr. W was horrified to learn this. (Later, when Melanie and I were home laying on her bed, she told me that was the first time she saw Dr. W tear up that day.)

"What were they doing?" he asked indignantly. "When those doctors burned the inside of your nose, they fried your nerve endings. You've got blockages in your in brain, abdomen, neck and spine. Nothing is flowing—it's all stagnant. Where there are blockages, stagnation forms. Where there's stagnation, disease forms."

I figured this was probably a good time to tell him about the sphenoid sinus disease and the whiplash injury I had in 1987, which required four years of intensive physical therapy and proliferant injections in my head, neck and shoulders.

Dr. W just regarded me woefully while he took it all in, then called his son in to do some cranial sacral testing on me. After working on me for several minutes, Josh confirmed that he could find no pulses.

"You see, it all started with your birth. That set you up. The nasal cauteries and the whiplash finished you off." Dr. W gave me a sad, sympathetic smile. "You never got a good breath. I see this in about 25 percent of the Lyme patients I treat. Traumatic birth—you never got a good breath," he said, thumping me lightly on the solar plexus.

To back up his point, he told me about a young Lyme patient whose parents brought her to see him. She had been crying incessantly for years. Dr. W's daughter, an acupuncturist who had been sitting in on the evaluation, said to him, "Dad, she'd damp," which besides stating the obvious, is a diagnosis in Chinese medicine.

She placed needles in the indicated points and within a minute the girl stopped crying. It turned out that she had a difficult birth, causing some sort of problem that left her in perpetual tears. She was treated by Dr. W and was now doing very well, all Lyme-related problems gone.

After regarding me for a few minutes, Dr. W went back to the blood slide. "I'm not sure what to do with you," he said at last. "You're the most difficult case I've ever had."

Melanie and I looked at each other, not for the first time, wondering what this meant for me. After what she had told me, I found this hard to believe. What about the people who came to him in wheelchairs? Certainly they were worse off than I was.

"You have so many problems, I don't know where to start. There's only one person who could help me with this—my mentor—but he's dead."

Dr. W called Adam back in. This time he told his son to bring in several isopathic remedies, which I was to hold while Adam checked the effect each had on my cranial rhythm. After being tested with each vial, Josh told his father which one had the most effect on me. Dr. W nodded.

"It's her sinuses," he concluded. He jumped up and beckoned us to follow him again. "We're going to give you some injections in your nose. They're going to completely open your whole sinus area," he said, smiling enthusiastically as he patted me on the arm. Though he was trying to be encouraging, I could see trepidation in Mel's eyes.

All of us went to the treatment room next door. I lay down on the table while Dr. W prepared the syringe. I was no stranger to nasty-looking needles, having gone through the two years of proliferant injections. I waited patiently as Dr. W and his son planned the attack. Mel watched on nervously.

It took but one injection to understand her fears. This pain trumped all others. It took every ounce of grit I could muster to keep from screaming. I can't remember exactly how many shots there were; Dr. W kept repeating "just one more..." about eight times.

After he had injected several areas starting from below my eye on both sides of my nose, he went in for the kill: two injections in the sensitive area at the bottom of each nostril. After the first side, I called a time-out so I could mop my face and work up my courage.

"You're doing great," Dr. W assured me. Melanie, who had been holding my jerking legs down, looked on with eyes brimming with tears of her own.

"How many more?" I asked weakly.

"Just a couple."

"Okay...I'm ready," I said, driving my nails into the soft parts of my hands. An abbreviated whimper escaped me as Dr. W did the other side. We all took a collective breath. *Thank God that was over.*

"How you doing?" Dr. W asked.

"Okay..."

"I'm going to get your tonsil pillars," Dr. W said, motioning for me to open my mouth wide by demonstrating the proper posture himself. I opened wide, bracing myself again.

"Did you hear that popping?" he asked. "Open your mouth again." I obliged him, setting off two loud pops. "You're going to need to get your bite reset," Dr. W said. "I'll give you a doctor's name before you leave."

The next shots he administered were the same shots that had annihilated Melanie. He stuck the needle somewhere deep in my month, not unlike what a dentist would do before drilling. After the excruciating pain of the nose shots, the tonsil pillars didn't faze me. Bam, bam a couple times on both sides of the mouth.

"That's it?" I asked, hesitantly.

"That's it," Dr. W replied happily. "They're not bad," he said, as he moved across to the door, beckoning me again with a wag of the head. I struggled to right myself, feeling as though I had been hit in the face by a flying porcupine. Once I was on my feet, I wobbled back to Dr. W's office, where he motioned for me to take a seat. Adam came in and went directly to the task of reading my cranial pulses.

"She's much more open. I can feel a decent pulse. I think she liked it," he said.

"Excellent," Dr. W said, grabbing my left middle finger for another poke.

We were in Dr. W's office for several hours. When Melanie and I finally emerged, everyone was gone. Before the receptionist left, Dr. W told her he needed to see me the next day. Even though I was thoroughly rung out and overwhelmed by the experience, I felt hopeful. At least he was doing something. And if the pain/gain theory was worth anything, then this would certainly have to help. Besides, the blood looked better; that had to be a good sign.

Back at Mel's house, we had a lot to digest. As far as the office went, I liked the overall feeling of the place—not hippie-dippie alternative; more dignified and well run, with a pervasive air of cheery confidence and a strong reliance on science, of the alternative sort. Dr. W seemed to have a real grasp of his diagnostic tools, and the ability to cut to the heart of the matter.

His approach to health issues was different than most, in that he did not believe in trying to kill the disease. Instead, his focus was on strengthening the body and the immune system so bacteria and other health-destroying organisms could live symbiotically in the body without making one sick.

He pointed out that we all have strep bacteria in our throats, yet we don't all have strep throat. He said the same was true for cancer. The reason these cells did not make most of us sick was because our immune systems were strong enough to keep these infections and diseases in check.

His theory was that injuries and surgeries weaken our bodies and restrict the flow of blood and energy, which in turn leads to blockages, stagnation and disease. Stress also played havoc with the body, especially the adrenal glands, which produce and regulate more than 40 hormones. When these hormones aren't being properly produced, all kinds of imbalances occur.

All of that was easy for me to accept. I had always believed I was essentially a healthy person, even in the throes of all my health problems. Things had gotten out of whack—thanks largely to stress—and my body was no longer able to hold the Lyme in check. And that was when I became symptomatic.

Dr. W had said he wasn't sure what to do with me; he'd been very upfront with that disclosure. But at the same time, he seemed to be making some kind of progress. And he was willing to keep trying.

When I had planned my trip to Nevada City, I was only able to book the one appointment. I had been warned by Melanie that treatment costs could run around $10,000 for Lyme-related cases. It was not a number I could bear to think about.

I had gone up there with an open mind, curious to see what my live blood could reveal. I was very happy to have gotten another appointment while I was up there because I was sufficiently intrigued and anxious to see if Dr. W could perform some of his wizardry on me. If he was game, so was I. I was too overwhelmed at the time to think about the expense. I was just going to take this one step at a time.

Dr. W had me come in the next morning prior to my appointment in order to be treated by his colleague, Dr. X, who was a cranial osteopath. Dr. X was very gentle, and so was his modality. For an hour, he placed his hands on various parts of my body and just held them there, only occasionally rocking or shaking the area.

After we were finished, he told me he had never encountered anyone who was so devoid of cranial pulses as I was. He said I was like the walking dead, barely tethered to this earth, and it was a marvel I was still functioning. He did however say that by the end of the session, he was able to conjure up a "wispy" pulse. At least that was a step in the right direction.

After Dr. X's appointment, I went down the hall to see Dr. W. He quickly got down to business. He took the blood samples, and after analyzing them he said, "It's her abdomen. Her intestines are tied up in knots. I still think it's her sinuses, but we'll do the abdomen first."

I was taken to the treatment room and given several injections, none particularly painful, but not exactly pleasant either. Nothing that compared to the nasal shots.

Our small entourage returned to Dr. W's office, where he took more samples of my blood. The difference was plainly evident. There was much less grainy matter (debris) in the background, and the cells themselves seemed more buoyant. Dr. W was clearly pleased.

As he maneuvered around the slide, more of those large, brilliant shapes appeared. Satisfied that he was getting somewhere with me, his son was called in again for more testing. Adam confirmed that he was getting stronger pulses.

During my next appointment, Dr. W had one of his technicians give me an MRT treatment, which they refer to as "German cupping." Metal cuffs, like shackles, were placed on my wrists and ankles while I laid face down. Then I felt a pulsing/vibrating sensation on my back.

Once that was over, I was taken to the reception area, where the tech placed tubes in my ears, then filled them with ozone to see if they could "get my system turned on." This was also a rather trippy sensation, but after the five canisters of ozone had been pumped in, I felt euphoric. I was high on bad air. Whoever thought of that? Back I waddled to Dr. W's office for more finger sticks.

We were in and out of Dr. W's office for hours again. I had more injections, this time in the Franckenhauser points. Back to his office for some pig stem cells, which I had to hold under my tongue for 5 minutes. Pig stem cells taste disgusting. Dr. W had given me some before we left his office the first day, and it was a taste I still hadn't acquired.

After each procedure, my blood was tested. It had improved throughout each day, only to be back to its awful-looking self the next morning.

Through cancellations and added hours, I managed to get four days of treatments on that first trip. I was sent home with vials of assorted stem cells (liver, thalamus, thymus, heart, eyes), boxes of capsules I had to alternate every week, and something called "cell therapy" that I had to inject myself with daily. I took all this stuff home to Santa Barbara, along with a flickering hope it could somehow make me better.

On my last day, Dr. W said to me, "You are going to get well. The reason I know this is because you want to get well. About 25 percent of the patients I see who have Lyme have become too identified with their disease. It becomes a part of who they are. You're not like that. I can tell you want to get well."

He was right about that; I wanted to get well more than anything.

LUCKY BREAK

While I was up in Nevada City submitting myself to Dr. W's unusual methods, we had a stroke of good fortune. After going in escrow four times and falling out three, the Palm Springs house finally sold.

As an investment, Casa Bonita was not a good one. All the sale did for us was stop the bleeding and put an end to all the work and aggravations associated with the property. Those two things alone had a huge impact, particularly for Guy. He no longer had to be involved in the rental process and the inevitable problems associated with an out-of-town vacation rental. We were both relieved. One less thing to worry about.

Now life was beginning to take on a familiar feel. We were back in our Summerland house, I wasn't working at a mortgage company, and we didn't have any vacation rentals to deal with. Having Casa Bonita sold lightened our financial burden, which in turn lightened our stress load. And to sweeten the pot even more, I had hope again of finally getting well. Things were headed in the right direction.

Once I got back home, I contacted the mother of the girl with Lyme disease Mel had seen at Dr. W's. Because their experience had been so positive, Laura was happy to share her daughter's story with me. Our conversation lasted an hour and was very informative.

What they had gone through as a family was astounding. Ironically, Jessica and I were both infected around the same time, back when it was still largely believed the disease didn't exist on the west coast. Even though Laura had taken her daughter to the hospital as soon as the bites were discovered, the doctor prescribed an inadequate dose of the wrong antibiotic. But Laura would not know that until years later.

In the meantime, Jessica, who was only six when she became infected, started having difficulty in school. She had trouble concentrating, and was put into Special Ed classes. At that point, Laura had no reason to suspect Lyme disease was the cause of the change in Jessica's aptitude.

It wasn't until much later, when alarming new symptoms appeared, that they began the tedious, expensive and unsatisfying quest to find out what was wrong with their daughter.

From what I've learned, teenagers afflicted with Lyme have more dramatic and baffling symptoms, which often include grand mal seizures, blindness, hearing loss, the inability to speak, and other devastating maladies. Over the course of Jessica's pursuit for a cure, she was hospitalized on numerous occasions due to "pain episodes."

As Laura recounted for me their harrowing journey to save their daughter's life, I saw a familiar pattern emerge. For several years, the family went from one doctor to another, one hope to another, and finally, when they were down to their last hope, they took a two-month trip to India, to a hospital they believed was Jessica's last chance of getting well.

Unfortunately, the treatments didn't bring about any improvement. Jessica continued to deteriorate. Laura told me that at one point she feared they would be coming home without her. While she sat in the hallway of the hospital trying to absorb her daughter's fate, an American woman sat down beside her. After inquiring about their reason for making the trip, the woman said, "If your daughter has Lyme disease, why isn't she seeing Dr. W?"

Laura was stunned. There they were, halfway around the world, and this stranger is telling her about a doctor who is only a five-hour drive from where they live. She got the information from the woman and called Dr. W's office as soon as they returned home. They were able to get a week's worth of appointments a month later.

By then, Jessica was not much more than a skeleton, confined to a wheelchair. After the first visit with Dr. W, she told her mom that if she couldn't open a bottle of water by her seventeenth birthday, she was going to kill herself. So much of her life had been nothing but suffering. She had had enough.

After the third day with Dr. W, when they were back at the hotel, Jessica astonished herself by cracking the seal on a bottle of water. Elated to the point of tears, she called Dr. W.

"It's okay, calm down…just tell me what happened," Dr. W said.

"I opened a bottle of water!" Jessica sobbed.

"Congratulations, kiddo. You're going to make it."

It took five monthly visits to see Dr. W before Jessica felt like a human being again. I asked Laura how Jessica was doing now.

"She just spent the day up at the hot springs with her friends, and now she's getting ready to go to the fair. She's almost off all three of her pain meds, and she's feeling great. No more seizures, no more wheelchair."

After literally travelling around the world to find help for their daughter, and spending unfathomable amounts of money, they at last had a happy, healthy teenager who had lost most of her childhood to a nightmare of a disease.

One thing Laura cautioned me against was travelling to Vancouver to see the dentist Dr. W recommended for resetting Jessica's bite.

"I love Dr. W, but I have to tell you that trip was a waste of time and money," she told me. "The treatments were $7,000, plus all our travel expenses. And to be honest, it didn't make any difference." I was relieved she had shared this with me. I knew when Dr. W gave me the referral that I couldn't afford such an extravagance, especially on top of everything else.

Talking to Laura was a gift she was happy to share with anyone faced with Lyme. When I hung up, I felt a warm hope growing in my chest. This girl had been through hell, and Dr. W had been able to make her well. If he could do this for Jessica, surely he could help me.

After our conversation, Laura emailed me three links, one of which was of a radio interview with Dr. W and three young Lyme patients he had helped. I listened to the program, amazed to hear these young adults talk about what they had been through and how they were doing now. It was more proof that if anyone could cure me, it had to be him.

My next trip to Nevada City was in October. As Guy and I hadn't had a vacation in years, he suggested a trip to San Francisco for my birthday. We worked it so we would drive up together, then afterwards I would take him to the airport and then drive to Nevada City, which is only about a two and a half hour trip.

On October 5th, I had an appointment with Dr. X. I arrived from San Francisco just in time. I was in good spirits and feeling relatively well. The next morning was a different story.

I don't know if it was because of all we had done in San Francisco (Guy was amazed by how much I had walked and how well I'd held up), but I barely had the strength to wash my hair. I felt completely exhausted. When I got to Dr. W's, I was feeling awful and strangely melancholy. I was on the verge of tears, for no reason.

When Adam took me into the treatment room for some injections, I asked him if he would be going with his parents to the hot springs to celebrate his father's birthday, which was a week after mine. Adam shook his head.

"No, my dad is a bear around his birthday. I'll let mom handle him."

"Your dad doesn't like birthdays?"

"He usually gets sick, which makes him very cranky."

"That's strange."

"Well, your birthday is actually the lowest point in the year for you—your body, your spirits. Everything is at its most vulnerable."

"Really?" I said. "It's my birthday today, and I feel horrible. I feel like I'm going to start blubbering any minute."

"Don't worry, it's normal. Your birthday and six months later—those are your two weakest times of the year."

The next day, I was in much better spirits. My blood was looking good, too. It seemed like we were making some progress. As with each appointment, I would be receiving injections; the only variable was where.

The smiling face I was wearing when I walked into the office was replaced shortly afterward with a mascara-streaked one, à la Alice Cooper. Just when I thought it was safe to enter the treatment room again, Dr. W announced he was going to give me the sinus injections. But this time he upped the ante.

In addition to all the points he had treated before, he tackled some other sinus points on my forehead, which caused all the waterworks. As soon as he injected those points, tears gushed from the corresponding eye. This time I didn't have my sister along to hold my legs down. It was just Dr. Needle and me.

After the first side, I had to call for a break. I sat up, chest heaving, trying to catch my breath. Dr. W handed me a tissue, which was hardly adequate for mopping up the flood damage.

As I panted and tried to steel myself for round two, Dr. W and I had a nice chat. He told me he had his nose broken several times while playing high school football and had received those same nose shots himself. He knew they were tough, but a doctor has to do what he has to do. I lay back down and weathered the assault the best I could, with much flesh clawing, but barely a whimper.

Even though I had an appointment with Dr. X after lunch, there was no way I could hang around looking like death's head. I staggered out to my car, feeling as though I'd been run over by a street cleaner, and drove back to my sister's. I washed my face and redid my makeup, and returned to the office looking reasonably human. Fortunately, Dr. X had never hurt me. He was the gentle giant to Dr. W's tiny warrior.

During one of my sessions with Dr. X, he asked me if, living in Santa Barbara as I do, I ever took walks on the beach. I told him I walk next to the beach, but never on it. He suggested I start walking *on* the beach, as there is no better way to reset one's adrenals.

After I got home, I thought about what Dr. X had said. *Why didn't I walk on the beach? It was right there. What was keeping me from walking down those steps to the sand?* Every day when I took my walk on the sidewalk above the shore, I would watch other people gaily walking on the sand in their bare feet.

One day, as I was walking by in my customary fashion, I thought *just do it—just take your shoes off and walk on the beach.* I stopped at the top of the stairs and took off my shoes. I walked down the steps and placed my feet in the sand. Those first steps made me light up inside. I was instantly filled to bursting with joy.

I'm nearly a California native, having moved here with my family when I was five. We lived in Huntington Beach, a short drive from the ocean. From our first trip down to the shore, we became completely beach crazy. It was hard to drag my brother, sister and me away.

So why, after that early bonding, did I not indulge in the basic pleasure of feeling the soft, warm sand between my toes? How had I become so detached from my old self that I couldn't even remember the long connection I'd had with the seashore?

I was giddy with pleasure as I waddled through the soft sand down to the water's edge. Instantly, I was taken back to those early years, when merely touching the sand would make us squeal with delight. There I was, a fifty-two year old woman, trying to hide the giggles of a five-year-old child. I walked as far as I could along the shore, until the rising tide forced me to turn around.

From that day forward, I took my walks on the beach, barefoot and beaming. It was the beginning of a whole new era for me, and it made me realize what I had been missing out on all those years of living *next* to the beach and not taking advantage of the healing properties of being *on* the beach.

CAN'T WIN FOR LOSING

After the second trip to see Dr. W, I was feeling not only hopeful, but good. Now that I had rediscovered walking *on* the beach, I would check the tides online as soon as I woke up. I would plan my day around walking during the low tides, and I would practically trot down to the beach.

Then one day, as I was happily making my way to the shore, I started getting a bad stomach ache. I hadn't had stomach issues in a long time. But all of the sudden, I had that horrible acid taste in my mouth, burning my lips, tongue, throat and esophagus, as though I'd swallowed turpentine.

Puzzled, I racked my brain trying to figure out the cause. The lunch I had prior to the walk was something I ate regularly: two scrambled eggs with prosciutto, goat cheese and spinach, followed by that killer, super-fattening Greek yogurt with the sidecar of honey. It couldn't be that; I ate it all the time.

The acid burn did not go away by the next day. In fact, it's never let up a minute for over two and a half years now. After the first few desperate days, I began worrying in earnest: *Oh, no...not this again.* I started trying everything I could think of to get the acid to calm down. I radically changed my diet, eating only very bland things: bananas, rice, oatmeal, steamed vegetables, applesauce. Nothing made a difference.

Because I'd had another endoscopy in January, I knew there was no point in going back to see Dr. J; after that second scope, his nurse conveyed the message that I had "functional dyspepsia" and there was no need to schedule an office visit. I had come to understand that this meant my acid problem was all in my head.

Desperate and lacking a traditional approach, I called Melanie; she always had good alternative advice. She did her research and called back with a list of supplements and teas that would take care of the problem.

In typical fashion, I went out and bought everything on the list: slippery elm capsules, chamomile and Pau d'Arco teas, papaya enzymes, Aloe Vera juice, chlorella, milk thistle seed extract and carrot juice, to name a few.

I've never been what you'd call a health nut, and drinking carrot juice is something I've avoided all my life. I'm more the champagne type. But desperate times call for desperate measures. I obediently gagged down the carrot juice and all the assorted "remedies," hoping against hope that they would do the trick.

After several weeks of trying the alternative arsenal, I went back up to see Dr. W. In regard to the new problem, he advised eating steamed vegetables and lots of dairy—yogurt, cheese and milk—to coat the stomach. This last directive was contrary to the advice given in Mel's book, and seemed to defy common sense, especially since an overabundance of fat seemed to be what set off this whole syndrome.

Now I was really starting to feel hopeless; the acid in my throat and mouth had been raging for two months, the most prolonged and persistent acid reflux bout I'd ever had. And even with all the other problems that continued to plague me, the acid problem now had my full attention.

There was very little I could eat, and even a stringent diet didn't make any difference. Everything burned from the esophagus up, around the clock, no matter what I did or ate. My greatest pleasure— eating—had now become my biggest nightmare. Going to a restaurant was a gastronomic minefield. In short, I was no fun anymore.

But that problem was of minor concern for Dr. W; he had much bigger dragons to slay. My blood, though usually quite good after a four-day stint, would invariably revert back to terrible when I was out of his care. He told me that if I lived close by, he'd have me in every week; it was the only way he could see ever getting ahead of all my various and complex problems.

But barring that, he had to make the best use of the time I was there, and then send me home with an array of isopathics, stem cells and a bag of needles for injecting the cell therapy.

Back in Santa Barbara, I spoke to Dr. Brad about Dr. W's concern regarding my popping jaws, and how my bite needed to be reset. Dr. W brought the subject up every time I went to see him. But there was no way I could travel to Vancouver and spend thousands of dollars to have it taken care of. But I didn't need to worry. Dr. Brad had me covered.

"I happen to be an expert at resetting bites," he told me.

Over the next several weeks, Dr. Brad worked on realigning my jaws. He had a special maneuver that fixed the problem without a whole lot of fuss or pain. When I went up to see Dr. W again, I was able to open my mouth without sound effects.

In March of 2010, I made my fourth pilgrimage up to Dr. W's. In December, Melanie had flown down and we drove up together, which meant I had to make the 500 mile drive back by myself. It was brutal, due in part to strong winds.

In March, when I braved the round trip solo, the wind was even worse. And to complicate matters, I had to drive up on four hours sleep, having been wide awake since 3 a.m.

Because I'd had so little sleep, I was in a world of hurt. After only two hours of driving, I couldn't imagine how I was going to last another six. I had my birthday playlist blaring in an effort to keep me alert and keep my spirits up. But I knew that alone wasn't going to pull me through.

What I needed was to shorten the length of the drive. So, as I drove along the open highway, I began to calculate how fast I would have to drive to shorten the trip to six hours. I had been zooming down the road at a comfortable 80–85 mph, and I figured if I could round it up to 90, I might shave off a couple hours. That would be just about doable; I figured that was the maximum amount of life I had left in me.

This plan would've worked, except for two oversights: I don't live in Germany, and Highway 101 is not the autobahn. There I zipped through the least-travelled stretch of 101, intent on making it to Nevada City before I croaked, oblivious to the Highway Patrol car travelling in the southbound lane. I became aware of him soon enough, as he swooped down on me like a Peregrine falcon on a witless vole.

He must've thought he had some big, bad fugitive from justice on his radar; the swiftness of his corralling me made my heart thump. I think he was a little disappointed and a little relieved to find a semi-frail 52-year-old woman at the wheel. His demeanor visibly softened when he saw that he wasn't going to have to yank me out of the car and handcuff me.

I think if I'd been up to it, I might've been able to appeal to his good nature by explaining that I was using my last ounce of willpower to get to up to see my doctor before I collapsed, but I just didn't have that kind of negotiating ability left in me. Besides, I'd been driving way too fast; I had earned the ticket fair and square.

The officer did feel sorry for me, though; he rounded down the ticket to say I'd only been going 10 miles over the speed limit, which would make me eligible for traffic school and save me a bunch of money. He also said that I wasn't "driving recklessly or anything, just cruising..." I took this as some sort of stamp of approval. I thanked him and let him blast off before I pulled back out onto the highway, belatedly mindful of the speed limit.

For the last two hours of the drive, I was screaming from the pain. Fortunately, Mel had made some chicken soup and took care of me from the moment I fell out of the Jeep.

In addition to the horrendous drive, the March trip was also hampered by nasty weather. It was raining and barely above freezing in the daytime. It didn't really matter; I was so beaten up, all I could manage was going to my appointments, coming back to Mel's and collapsing again. But the visits to Drs. W and X proved to be very interesting, with new twists and insights I hadn't bargained on.

Since my last visit in December, Dr. W had taken on a new assistant, who sat in on all his sessions and administered the shots and other protocols. Dr. W recapped my history for her in broad brushstrokes, highlighting the components he found most telling.

When I told him I was still having the acid problem, his assistant asked if I ate foods containing gluten. I told her I'd stopped eating gluten about two years before the acid attack started, just to see if it would help with the inflammation throughout my body.

Later on, while trussing me up to some sort of machine to measure inflammation, the assistant, who was a trained nurse, told me about a simple blood test that could determine if I had celiac disease.

This was welcome news for me; though I knew I felt better once I stopped eating gluten, I half-wondered if this was because I had celiac disease. I really didn't think I did; but if I could find out for sure I didn't have celiac, I wouldn't have to strenuously avoid eating anything with gluten. I could eat a sandwich when nothing else was available without worrying about the consequences. I thought it was worth finding out.

After lunch, I came back for my appointment with Dr. X. When we were finished, he asked me if I'd ever seen a "medical intuitive." *No, I'd never even heard off one before.* "Well, you will tomorrow," he said, as he walked out of the room.

I didn't think too much of this prediction, as it was fairly common for Dr. W to have various medical professionals coming to observe and learn his unorthodox methods. I imagined that at some point the next day our paths would cross.

I didn't attach any significance to a possible encounter until I went to the front office to settle up. Dr. X, phone in hand, asked if I could make a 10:00 appointment the following morning. Evidently, I was going to go see this medical intuitive, not the other way around.

I had back to back appointments with Drs. W and X starting at 11:00, so I cautiously accepted, provided I'd have time. No problem. It was all settled. Dr. X wrote down the woman's name, number and address on his card and sent me on my way, giving me no idea what I'd just agreed to.

The following morning found me hunting for the medical intuitive's office in a frigid downpour. When I finally tracked down the number I was looking for, I shook out my umbrella and quickly stepped inside the office.

The waiting area was on the small side, but bright and cheerful enough. Had there not been two women standing in the hallway between the two treatment rooms, I might've continued to erroneously believe I had an appointment with a medical specialist. But there was something about the garb and the mannerisms of these two women engrossed in a private conversation that gave me my first clue I wasn't in Kansas anymore.

As I tried to contain my dripping to the doormat, I waited patiently while the women conferred. I had no wish to intrude on their conversation, or for that matter, to eavesdrop. But as I was standing no more than eight feet away with nowhere else to turn, it was unavoidable.

When one of the women asked the other for advice on which Tarot card to use in a particularly vexing situation, the light finally dawned. Before I could give myself a mental face slapping, one of the women turned and asked me my name.

"Oh, you're mine!" she exclaimed pleasantly. She smiled and beckoned for me to follow her. As soon as I passed into the room, she excused herself for a moment. This gave me a chance to pull myself together and stifle my laughter. I could not believe what I had gotten myself into this time. As I looked around at the skulls and roses and unusual artifacts, I marveled once again at the lengths I was willing to go to get well.

Okay, so I'm a little slow. Back in Santa Barbara, we don't really bandy around the term "intuitive" in the professional sense. The word simply didn't have that connotation for me. Throw "medical" in front of it and my mind conjures up a professional in the field of medicine. Duh. This was Nevada City; I should've known better. But what was I going to do now? I didn't even know how I was going to pay for this. Did psychics take credit cards?

When Samantha came back into the room, I tried to act as natural as possible. I hadn't yet decided if I was going to feign total ignorance or just jump in and act like I go to psychics all the time. Problem was, I was nervous and I'm sure it showed.

Samantha coaxed me to have a seat at the table in the middle of the room. She sat across from me and asked me to give her my hand. The table was wide, and I found it uncomfortable to extend my arm that far.

"No problem. I'm going to come and sit next to you," Samantha said as she planted herself closer to me, my hand still in hers. "Okay...," she said gently. "It's okay...just relax..." She looked straight into my eyes and my first thought was *NO! Don't look in there!*

From my very first appointment with Dr. W, he had been warning me there were possible emotional issues complicating my recovery. Now, I'll put up with almost any kind of physical torture in the name of healing, but stay the hell away from my psyche, okay? I've got my issues, like anyone else, and I'm a firm believer in leaving the past alone.

But when Dr. W continued to bring this up during every visit, I knew at some point I was going to have to put on my scuba gear and go deep, down into my soul and unlock the door that kept all my demons at a safe distance. And in fact, I had just done that—at 3:00 in the morning when I couldn't sleep, the day I drove up there.

Part of the reason I was so averse to poking around in the past was that I was pretty certain I had already made my peace with the monsters in my closet. When I realized I wouldn't be able to go back to sleep that night, I got up and decided—for the sake of thoroughness—to reexamine those painful incidences in my life, making sure I hadn't hidden anything from myself. If there was any chance something like this was keeping me from a medical breakthrough, I needed to confront it and get it out of the way, once and for all.

I sat on one of our guest beds, in the semi-dark, and performed a mental "perp walk." I trotted out everything I could find lurking in the nether regions of my mind, turning each incident over carefully, looking for anything that would make me wince with pain. No, nothing I hadn't put to rest; no sore spots that I could find.

Determined to face Dr. W with a clean emotional slate, I went back over it all one more time. And there it was, right in the middle of everything—something so obvious, yet something I was certain I had no residual problem with: my father.

I don't know if it was the shock of finally realizing I had been abandoned by my father when I was twelve, or if it were due the fact that I was up in the middle of the night, wracked with pain, but as soon as I had the epiphany, I started to cry.

The thing that struck me was my tears weren't caused by old wounds; I wasn't crying so much for the loss of my father as I was for my father's sake. I won't go into all the gory details, but that moment was the first time I was able to see and understand a little of what it must've been like for my father, to leave our family forever. I wasn't crying for being left behind; I was truly grieving for what it would've been like to be in his shoes.

That morning, when I strapped myself in and headed up 101, I was confident I had *really* dealt with all my issues. There wasn't anything left that could harm me emotionally anymore. I had a new understanding of my father and no longer feared his memory. In fact, I was happy to announce to Dr. W the next morning that he was right: I had been toting around some emotional baggage I hadn't been aware of. But I'd found the problem and taken care of it.

Even though I felt moderately confident about my emotional well-being, I felt distinctly uncomfortable having Samantha peering deeply into my eyes. There was something about her gaze that made it clear I was at a definite disadvantage; I had never done anything like this before and she did it for a living.

Plus, I was still trying to put Dr. X and this "medical intuitive" together. He was a board certified osteopath and she was a psychic. Why was I here? Was she really going to look into my eyes and find some medical problem that all the doctors had missed? Or…was she going to conjure up all my demons and have them dance around the room?

Samantha got right away that I was uncomfortable. Unfortunately, all her efforts at making me relax made me feel more self-conscious. What would Guy say about all this hocus-pocus? I couldn't even let myself think about that. I was pushing it with all the other alternative stuff as it was.

Besides, *I* wasn't exactly on board with this kind of shenanigans. But there I was, my hand being caressed by a complete stranger who collected skull motifs and communicated with otherworldly beings. *Oh, brother.*

When Samantha started to "see" things, I got a deeper sinking feeling—not because she had hit a nerve, but because I couldn't imagine what she was talking about.

"Your gallbladder is going to have to come out at some point," she said. *My gallbladder?* I'd had an ultrasound of my gallbladder twice, and nothing was found. This was turning out to be more of a sham than I first suspected. But suddenly her probe changed course, as if something had just popped up on her radar screen.

"Your mother lives in an assisted living situation," she said.

"No, actually, my mother lives alone and does everything herself, and she's very stubborn about it," I replied. Samantha looked unconvinced.

"But I see her place…it's in a cluster of small houses…"

"Well, yes…she lives in a cooperative development."

"And there are many of these houses…like squares."

"Yes, there are."

"There are lots of other people around, but she keeps to herself…"

"Yes, that's true."

"She's emotionally cold, your mother."

"Umm..."

"Your mother has never been there for you," Samantha said matter-of-factly, looking me straight in the eye, an expression of compassionate pity on her face. She knew she was right, even before I did. It took me seeing the confidence in her eyes to understand she'd got my number. It wasn't just a guess. It was the one thing I'd never wanted to admit to myself, let alone anyone else. But there was no way I could deny it, and realizing this made me burst into tears.

Samantha set a box of tissues in front of me and let me blow my nose before taking my hand back. She wasn't finished yet. It didn't take her long to tap back into her source.

"You and your sister have a difficult relationship with your mother," she continued. I held her gaze, but didn't say anything. *Could she really see all this?* She then told me specifics of our shared past, things that she had no way of knowing. Hearing these observations from someone who didn't even know me, I started sobbing again.

It's okay, it's okay," Samantha said. "Just let it out." I withdrew my hand from hers and helped myself to more tissues. After I had calmed down, Samantha took my hand back and resumed her investigation. Her findings were not good.

I listened as she recounted details about my relationship with my mother, and my mother's relationship with Melanie, cringing inside. *How was it possible for her to know these things?* I just couldn't understand how this worked, yet I couldn't deny what she was saying was true. I was more upset about what Melanie had gone through than I was about myself.

"Don't worry about your sister," Samantha said, sitting back. "She's got your mother in a box," she said, using her hands to form a square. "She's okay. She knows how to protect herself."

After several more minutes of this kind of disclosure, Samantha shifted her search to other areas of my life. She told me things about Guy, about Melanie. She told me the name of the one prescription I took, and told me to increase the dosage to three a day.

She also told me yogurt, milk and cheese would be good for my stomach problems. When the session was over, she took my credit card, which she was all set up to take, and we set up a phone appointment for the following week.

As I left the office of psychic phenomenon, I felt like I'd been through an emotional whirlwind. But there was no time to ponder any of this; I had to go straight to my appointment with Dr. X, who was curious to know if my meeting with Samantha had shed any medical insights. I told him what she had said about my gallbladder. I also had learned that both Drs. W and X "consulted" with Samantha from time to time, and vice versa.

While Dr. X worked on me, I lay there wondering about all this new stuff I'd just been exposed to. I'm a born cynic, and even though Samantha had pulled some impressive information out of her hat, I had to wonder how that was possible.

For starters, it wasn't any kind of stretch for her to assume that I had a mother who was of the age to be in assisted living. Even if she had figured my age to be ten years younger, and guessing that my mother was at least in her late sixties, early seventies, it wouldn't be unreasonable to assume that she needed outside care. She had probably about 50% chance of being right.

And mothers and daughters are notorious for having difficult relationships. Again, the odds would be at least 50/50 of this being the case. So, she hits those two points and she's got me hooked. How many daughters feel their mothers are difficult, even unloving? I could probably set up shop on these two assumptions alone.

The way she described the place where my mother lives, and "seeing" the little white pill I take, those two facts were harder to dismiss. And the details she knew about our relationship; all those disclosures were eerie, to say the least. This presented a real challenge for me: do I throw out my skepticism about all things paranormal and embrace everything she had told me? I wasn't quite ready to do that.

To add to the oddness of my session with Samantha was her assertion that there were many beings out in the universe that loved me. There was this great, unquestioning love I should open up and feel. If I could get past the weirdness of this supposition, I guess it would be comforting to think the universe loved me...right? But then again, don't all of us need heaps of unconditional love? Isn't that just the balm for a troubled mind and body?

All in all, I have to say what I took away from my session with Samantha was pretty mixed. I did report to Dr. W that I had gone to see her on the advice (sort of) of Dr. X. Dr. W was quite pleased to hear this. When I told him her opinion regarding my gallbladder, Dr. W took her prognostication very seriously.

"You've got gallstones, yes. That makes sense. The liver can't store the bile in the gallbladder. Your stomach doesn't have the acid to breakdown your food. You get all backed up. I can fix this," he said, with a confident wag of his finger. "I'll give you instructions to take home."

Later that day, when I was finally at Mel's, I gave her the rundown on my meeting with the "medical intuitive." As I relived the experience, we both were awed by the eeriness of her observations. Regardless of how she arrived at the insights, that there was now a third party privy to the skewed nature of our relationship with our mother made us feel oddly vindicated.

At the same time, it had reopened old wounds and made us reexamine them from a stranger's viewpoint. But most of all, it made me look at myself. There was really no denying my mother couldn't treat me the way she did unless I let her. So why, after all I'd been through, was I still going back for more?

Mel shared with me how she had come to the same realization many years ago. In order for her to become a whole, well-adjusted person, she had to keep our mother at arm's length. From then on, their contact was much more superficial. I knew about this to some degree, but I hadn't understood the extent of Mel's disengagement from her. With what I now knew about their past, I completely understood Mel's decision.

For many years my relationship with my mother had been lopsided. Like Melanie, I too had felt I was responsible for my mother's happiness and wellbeing. Unlike Mel, who had enough sense to pull out of the role of emotional dumping ground/whipping post, I had blindly clung to my duty as child/parent.

The more discontented my mother became, the harder I tried to make her happy. Her unbroken line of health problems kept me on a constant search for remedies and treatments that could alleviate all her suffering.

But what I had been studiously ignoring for decades was that I was powerless to change my mother's life, no matter how much I wanted to or how hard I tried. Stubbornly hanging on to this desperate hope had not been good for either of us. Now I finally realized this. I had to pull back the way Melanie did. I couldn't keep setting myself up for failure, and I couldn't let her misery drain the life out of me.

If nothing else, the trip to the psychic had launched an honest discourse between my sister and me regarding our mother. It opened my eyes to the reality that I was essentially beating my head against a wall.

All my efforts with my mother had not resulted in a good relationship. If I dropped my end of the charade, my mom would still be miserable, but I would no longer be consumed by angst over her deep unhappiness and her myriad of health concerns.

As we lay there on Mel's bed, a sort of peace and understanding came over me. Mel had already exorcised her demons. All those years, I had been unaware of all the emotional strife between her and our mother.

But now my eyes were open; I saw the destructive pattern that my mom and I had fallen into, and how detrimental it was for me. Now I would have to take control over my emotional wellbeing with the same sense of determination I focused on getting rid of Lyme. I needed to get well, body and soul.

MARCH MADNESS

The drive back from Nevada City was so brutal, I knew I could never make the trek again. It had undone all the good I had received from my treatments. Next time, I would have to fly.

The take-home remedy Dr. W prescribed for the gallstones I supposedly had consisted of drinking a hideous mixture of grapefruit juice and olive oil. To this day, I can't say the words *olive oil* without getting a queasy feeling. But the elixir was only part of the scheme.

After choking down a tall glass of the aforementioned drink, I had to rub olive oil on my stomach, top that with a layer of plastic wrap, top that with a towel soaked in olive oil, topping all that with more plastic wrap and a heating pad. I then had to lay there, the revolting beverage heating up in my stomach, for an hour. If you ever want to make yourself extremely nauseated, this is an excellent way to do it.

This guaranteed cure for gallstones had to be performed for three consecutive days. On the third day, there was a very low tide in the afternoon, which I wanted to take advantage of. I would be back in plenty of time to gag down the last repulsive dose and hopefully recover from the nausea before dinnertime.

Despite what I had waiting for me at home, I was exuberant when I hit the beach. It was a glorious day, very warm and sunny. As I had been doing for five months now, I went charging over the sand in bare feet.

Five minutes into my walk, I hit my middle toe on a small rock. Even over the crash of the waves, I heard the crack. The pain was so instantaneous and intense, I knew right away I had broken it. In lieu of screaming—there were people behind me—I bit down on the inside of my cheek and sunk my nails into the fleshy part of my butt while I reeled from the pain.

I had put considerable effort into getting to the beach at just the right time to take advantage of the low tide, which would allow me to walk on my favorite stretch of the coastline, something I don't get to do very often. It was too nice a day to waste. I gave myself a minute to get over the initial pain, then I hobbled for the balance of the hour-long walk, broken toe be damned.

I made it all the way, but not without pain. Still, I made it. When I got home, I slathered arnica all over my discolored and throbbing toe, then prepared my yummy drink. Once I greased myself and got all ready to make myself feel really sick, I put an icepack on my foot and the heating pad on my stomach. While I lay there, turning green, I thought about all the stuff that needed to be done in the next two days before everyone arrived for my mom's 80th birthday party.

The familial epiphany I'd had while up in Nevada City, though necessary, came at a rather inconvenient time. Now Mel and I had to suck it in and act like everything was just fine between our mother and us, when it definitely wasn't. Too much had come up in our talks that I hadn't been able to come to terms with yet.

As this was a milestone birthday, Brad and Alice would be coming down, and so would Mel's son, Trevyn. Though Guy would be on a trail ride that weekend, he planned on leaving camp to drive down for the lunch, then drive back afterwards.

Josiah and Justine were also going to do their best to make it, though they were moving to Santa Barbara that day. But in any event, this would have to be a happy occasion. The only way I could see managing that would be to don a cheerful mask and put up an imaginary wall to keep my mother at a safe distance.

Brad and Alice came down the night before the others. This gave us some nice time alone together. Over cocktails and dinner, I felt compelled to share some of my newfound insights with my brother. Being the youngest and the only male, Brad has always enjoyed a different kind of relationship with our mother, so I had to be diplomatic about how I approached the subject.

It turned out they were already aware of the history between Mel and our mom. I was surprised, but also relieved that I didn't have to be the one to enlighten them. So, we were all on the same page, more or less, and that was helpful. Mel and I could play our parts while still being detached enough to not be dragged down by our mom. It was very important to keep myself from reverting to the old habit of constantly trying to right my mother's world.

With Brad, Alice and Trevyn there, it was relatively easy for Melanie and me to keep our distance. In fact, it was actually easier for us to enjoy ourselves and to promote a festive ambience, now that I had sorted out my feelings.

I had booked a private room at our mother's favorite restaurant and had brought in special bouquets to place on the table. Because of her age, my mother's orders had been no gifts, unless it was something she could eat. Mel and I stretched the criteria to include orchids, which she is very fond of. We placed outstanding specimens around the room, and when she walked in, she was delighted by all the flowers.

The lunch went off without a hitch and she was very contented to have us all there, despite the fact that Guy, Josiah and Justine weren't able to make it after all. She was happy and we were happy.

Whew! Mel and I thought, as Brad, Alice and Trevyn took her home. We had made it through her special day without ruining it for her and without it turning into a maudlin pity-party. It occurred to me that it was harder for her to act out if she didn't have a receptive audience to play to. This signified that I was taking a big step in the right direction.

To people who have or had a wonderful relationship with their parents, I imagine it is hard to understand my chilly attitude toward my mother. But it hadn't always been that way. I used to hold my mother in the highest regard and thought of her as a saint.

After all, every bad circumstance to ever befall her had been someone else's doing. Not hers. Never hers. She was just a helpless innocent with no will of her own, too good for this cruel word. I truly believed this for decades, which is why I tried so hard to make her life better—for decades. I was never able to succeed, and I finally understood why.

That I was now able to see her obvious flaws was important. She should've never been the main worry in my life. She should've been my mother, and I should've been her daughter, not her emotional slave. Now it would be possible for us to have a more healthy relation-ship, as long as I could keep us from relapsing into lifelong habits.

Unfortunately, if I wanted to discuss this awakening with her as a way to better our relationship, it would've been guaranteed to end in a horrible scene where she would breakdown and recount the litany of misfortunes in her life, reliving the horror of them and never seeing my point. We had been through this every time she was challenged in any way. Any attempt at open dialog would feel like an attack on her and it would've left me with those old feelings of remorse. At the age of 80, I would never change her. The only thing I could do was change me.

The Breaking Point

In May 2010, Guy and I celebrated 30 years together. Though Guy was busy with work and I was not doing well, I still thought it was important we commemorate this milestone. I was definitely feeling the passage of time and realizing how necessary it is to celebrate all the meaningful markers in our lives.

In that spirit, we went to New Orleans, the place where our relationship got its start. We ate and drank and rambled around all our favorite haunts, reviving old memories of living in the Quarter together.

Before our trip to New Orleans, Guy had twisted my arm to make an appointment with the gastroenterologist again. It had been seven months since the continuous burning in my esophagus started, and it was still going strong. I had tried every non-prescription drug available to treat the condition, plus several prescription drugs, with no improvement. When we returned from New Orleans, Guy insisted on accompanying me to the appointment.

Even though I had protested, I was glad Guy came along so he could witness the skepticism I had encountered for years. As I recounted the story of the sudden acid attack, I could see Dr. J shift uncomfortably as he mentally dug in to rebuff my complaints. His obvious opposition to my assertions was not lost on Guy, who came to my defense by asking if it would hurt to check out my esophagus, just to be sure.

"We can do the test again, but I'm a hundred percent sure it's Irritable Bowel Syndrome."

"And what about checking her gallbladder?"

"We can do another ultrasound," Dr. J said, clearly trying to placate us, despite his opinion.

I told him about the new health wrinkle that had me running to the bathroom five to nine times a day. I explained how it had started after our trip to New Orleans, and had been going on for two weeks. He said it was possibly due to something I had eaten or a bug I had picked up. If it continued another week, I should give him a call.

Back in his office a week later, we discussed the problem again. I'd had time to do a little research online before this second appointment, and I had discovered something called microscopic colitis, a disease where white blood cells line the colon, preventing the absorption of nutrients. This fit what I was experiencing. For once, Dr. J agreed with me.

"Are you thinking this is a possibility because of the Lyme?" I asked. He said yes. I found this significant because I wasn't sure he really believed I had Lyme disease. He told me the only way to check for this was to do a Sigmoidoscopy—sort of a mini colonoscopy—to collect a biopsy. We made the appointment for two weeks later.

Meanwhile, it was party time. Guy's 60th birthday was fast approaching. Unlike turning 30, 40 or 50, turning the ripe old age of 60 didn't put Guy in the mood for extravagant travel, or anything else for that matter. He would've just as soon forgotten the whole thing.

In the end, he decided all he really wanted to do on his birthday was to have his family around him. The stoicism with which he faced this event would've given one the impression he was preparing to leave this world for the next. (I can make light of his trepidation because my 60th is still years away).

To make his wish come true, Emma, Dave and Stella would come from New York to pay their respects. Guy's sister, Maria, and her daughter, Lacee, would fly in from New Orleans. Fortunately, Josiah, Justine and the kids were already living in Santa Barbara.

Prior to everyone's arrival, our good friends, the Cunninghams and the Youngs, took us out to dinner to the restaurant Guy used to own, the place where we first met. It was a very nostalgic period, all these trips down memory lane. But it was good—for both of us—to reflect on what we had done these last three decades.

For me, this was a chance to put my life into perspective. It was very soothing to recall what life had been like prior to Lyme; it gave me a comforting feeling to remember how vital I once felt and how good our partnership had been for both of us. Being able to look back at all your accomplishments and experiences is one of the few good things about getting older. I'm sure there are more; I just haven't figured out what they are yet.

Now that we had a significant gathering on our hands, I decided this called for a proper celebration, one that wouldn't feel too extravagant or make Guy feel conspicuous. I arranged for a caterer, a French chef we had known since the late 70s, to come and prepare a sumptuous dinner for the eight adults among us.

It was an incredible feast, one that had us oohing and ahhing all through the dinner, which lasted for hours. Guy brought some great wines out of his cellar. Philippe and his crew prepared everything in our kitchen, and took care of all the serving and cleaning. It turned out to be a perfect evening. Everyone was full of good spirits, including the birthday boy, who was now realizing it wasn't so bad to turn 60 after all.

One day while Emma, Dave and the baby were still staying with us, my mother called to ask if I could drive her to the doctor's. I said I would and asked her what was wrong. She said she didn't know, but she felt terrible—very weak and dizzy.

Dr. Y was very kind and compassionate with her. She listened intently as my mom described the pain she was having on the left side, starting from her shoulder, up the side of her face to the top of her head. She was so distraught, she broke down and cried twice as she described all the trouble she'd been having in recent years. Dr. Y was very sympathetic and did her best to calm my mother down and keep her focused on the current symptoms.

During this hour and a quarter visit, I attempted to supply Dr. Y with all the pertinent information she needed to help diagnose my mother's condition. Unfortunately, I had my own issues to deal with, which were random and basically uncontrollable. There were several times when I almost had to dash out of the room in search of the facilities.

Between the constant false alarms, I had at least two minor meltdowns. The hot flashes that had been plaguing me for over a year brought with them a sudden nausea and a dizzy feeling that almost laid me flat. I held things together as best I could, praying I would make it out of there without embarrassing myself, while trying to remember everything Dr. Y said so I could remind my mother afterwards.

Given my mother's complicated medical history, Dr. Y felt she had no choice but to err on the side of caution and have my mother completely checked out. When the test results came back, she called my mother in for another visit.

Her appointment was scheduled during the time I was to be at Dr. J's, so my mom drove the short distance herself. After I'd gotten the news from Dr. J that I indeed had microscopic colitis, I went across the street to Dr. Y's office.

When I walked in, Dr. Y was in the front office on a call. She signaled for me to wait while she left a message. My mom was nowhere in sight. Dr. Y had just gotten off the call and was explaining to me that my mother was scheduled for surgery early the next morning when my mom returned from the lab across the way. *Surgery? What did I miss?*

Dr. Y explained that she suspected my mother had temporal arteritis, the swelling of the temporal artery that could lead to very serious problems if left untreated. My mother had to be at the hospital by 7:30 to fill out the admittance forms. From there, we would go see the surgeon, then back to the hospital to prep for the surgery, which would last about an hour or so.

As Dr. Y relayed all this to me, I glanced at my mother, who suddenly seemed so small and frail. I was given a list of instructions to follow, along with prescriptions I would need to fill that afternoon. I walked my mom to her car as we discussed this latest development. I took her prescriptions to be filled, then went over the instructions with her very carefully. She was to have nothing to eat after 8pm, but she could take her heart medication with water in the morning.

After I made sure she was okay, I dropped off the prescription Dr. J had given me. The pharmacy didn't have the medication on hand, so it wouldn't be ready until the next day. Once I was back home, I called Melanie and Brad to give them an update, though I was still pretty sketchy about what was going on. I promised to call them when the surgery was over.

When Guy got home, I had lots to tell him. I finally had a chance to digest my appointment with Dr. J. The good news for me was that microscopic colitis was treatable with drugs. Within a few weeks, it should be a thing of the past.

When I picked my mom up the next morning, I asked her if she wanted me to get her some food for later, figuring she'd be starving by the time I got her home. She said no, she'd eaten a few arrowroot biscuits before she'd taken her medicine. I looked across the car at her in dismay.

"Mom, you weren't supposed to have anything to eat!" I said, tempted to turn around and take her home. I found myself wondering how much longer she was going to be able to live on her own. "Don't you remember?"

"They're just little bitty things. That shouldn't be a problem," she insisted. I sighed, had a hot flash and kept driving.

It wasn't until we met with the surgeon that I got a clue what was happening. The surgeon wasn't going to fix her temporal arteritis; she was merely going to do a biopsy of the artery and send it to the lab for testing. We wouldn't know for at least a week if my mom had this condition or not.

While performing her pre-op examination, the surgeon wanted to verify that my mother had had nothing by mouth since 8pm. I read the exasperation on her face when I broke the news to her that my mom had eaten a few crackers just prior to our visit. I watched mutely as my mother tried to assure her that they were *very small* crackers. All I could do was apologize and wait for her decision. Then I worried; should *I* be the one to call the whole thing off? She was my mother, after all.

As the doctor began lecturing us on the hazard of giving general anesthesia with food in the stomach, my mother went into a dither of her own.

"I can't have general anesthesia," she said, directing her tizzy more to me than the surgeon. "The last time I had it, I just knew I could never be put all the way under again. I didn't think I was going to come out of it," she said dramatically, her face becoming blotchy with agitation. *Well, this was a fine mess.*

"Is there any chance you can do the procedure with local anesthesia?" I asked. This idea got my mother's vote right away.

"Local would be much better for me," she lobbied as the doctor mulled this over.

"I'll be cutting into the temporal artery that runs right here...along your temple. I have to pull the vein out and cut out a section, then sew the two ends together," she said doubtfully. All eyes were on me suddenly, as if I were the one who had to make the call.

"It's up to you, Mom." My mother hemmed and hawed and finally decided she'd be okay doing the procedure without being put under. That settled, we went back over to the hospital for the prep.

While my mother was in surgery, I was welcome to wait in her room, the main advantage of that setup being I would have a private bathroom at my disposal. Good thing. But I soon grew antsy and had to wander.

Sometime after 1:00, they brought my mother back to her room. As I sat there watching her while she rested, it occurred to me the buffer I had carefully erected to keep a safe distance between us had been whisked away with one call for help. Now, here I was, back at her beck and call, tending to her needs as if the revelations up in Nevada City had never happened.

I had absolutely no qualms about caring for my mother. The rub came from only being able to share her company when it was in situations like this. It used to be she would let me take her to lunch or a movie, or take her out to dinner with us when Guy pressured me to pressure her.

But that kind of contact had ceased years ago, unless it was with Melanie when she came to visit. It was a different story with Brad; they would get up to all kinds of outings when he came to town. Maybe it was because I was the oldest; maybe she was raised to view the first born as the caregiver, though it had been her younger siblings who had taken care of her own parents as they got older.

Whatever the reasons behind our mother-daughter dynamic, this was the only role I was allowed to play in her life, and one I accepted without thinking. All I had ever wanted was for her to be happy. She liked it when I called her once or twice a week, and would always sincerely thank me for calling. Our conversations were always a combination of rehashing all her old grievances and current annoyances.

I didn't fault her for being the way she was, nor was I jealous of my brother's relationship with her. I'm just grateful she didn't abandon us when we were little, though her life would've been much easier. So

I did my duty as her daughter, but now I had to be careful not to let her usurp my life.

Seven hours after we first arrived at the hospital, I was finally able to take my mom home. I dropped off new prescriptions for her and, zoned-out and wracked with pain, I completely forgot to stop at my own pharmacy.

Before the results of the biopsy came back, Dr. Y had us get in to see the ophthalmologist. Since the day her doctor became concerned she might have temporal arteritis, every new symptom, real or imagined, gave my mom great anxiety. The more anxious she became, the more pain she was in.

The day we went to the eye doctor she was a nervous wreck. She nearly hyperventilated on the short drive to Dr. S's office. As was the case in the last several doctors' appointments, I had to be the liaison between the doctor and my befuddled mother.

When any direct questions were put to her, my mom—who was not-so-secretly delighted by all the attention she was getting—would prattle on about unrelated matters, missing the point of the queries altogether. A couple of minutes into any appointment, the doctors would invariably start turning to me for the answers.

Okay, my mom was 80 years old—what did I expect? Sooner or later she was going to start losing her touch, right? But in truth, she was still sharp as a tack when we weren't sitting in the doctor's office with people fussing over her.

While my mother was blathering on about how the nurse at the hospital had told her she'd never seen SO MUCH HAIR IN HER LIFE!, I sat there fielding the doctor's questions, sweating profusely and wondering if I could make it out of there without having an accident.

During the examination, Dr. S turned to me and asked why Dr. Y suspected temporal arteritis; my mother showed no signs or symptoms of the disease. I was at a loss for an answer. I hadn't been in the room when this whole drama began. It was quite clear that Dr. S did not concur with this diagnosis. It was no surprise to me when the biopsy came back negative.

While back in Dr. Y's office for the follow-up, our relationship took a turn for the worse. Dr. Y was relieved by the test results, yet at a loss on how to treat my mother's pain.

My mom was very discouraged and started crying. I felt so badly for her because I knew how frustrating it is to have problems no one knows how to fix. Dr. Y was very patient, letting my mom vent her frustrations, which became far-flung and rambling.

All Dr. Y's attempts at trying to find a rational means of treating the pain made my mother more agitated and combative. She started raging against one of our mutual doctors, calling him a sadist. I sat there in horror as she continued to slander a man who was so gentle, it was completely against his nature to hurt someone. I stammered as I tried to defend the doctor's good name.

"He's a sadist!" my mother cried out again, working herself into a frenzy as she gave this bizarre performance for her doctor's benefit. I was mortified.

To my immense relief, Dr. Y took the situation in hand. In a calm voice, she explained that if my mother's pain and disabilities were as bad as she claimed, then it was time to take a look at a different kind of living situation. And that might mean the loss of her freedoms, privacy and the right to drive.

Dr. Y's words acted like a magic spell. Instantly, my mother sat up straighter; gone were the theatrics and the teary, feeble appearance. It was as though everything that had just transpired had never happened.

"I'm fine, I'm fine," she said hastily. Just like that, she was cured. It was a miracle.

As we exited the examination room, we passed through the reception area filled with waiting patients. When we got there, it was empty. Our appointment should've taken less than twenty minutes. We had been in there over an hour and a half.

Once outside, my mom's mood turned surly. I was catching her wrath, though I couldn't figure out why. During the short drive back to her house, the atmosphere bristled with tension. Whenever I said something to her, she pretended she couldn't hear me, making me repeat myself.

When I pulled up to her building, she got out and slammed my car door with all her might, and walked away without another word. On the drive home, I felt like I had an anvil on my chest.

As soon as I had gotten home and lay down, I'd called my sister to give her an update. "I can't do it anymore," I said to Melanie. "I just can't be around her. She sucks the life out of me." I was beside myself;

I was in a lot of pain and I felt demoralized. When my mother started ranting in an almost hysterical fashion, I'd been ashamed she could act that way in public. Normally, she saved that kind of harangue for her kids.

As I lay there talking to Mel, it hit me that not once in the three weeks I'd been chaperoning her to her appointments had she asked me how I was doing. It didn't matter what I was going through as long as I was there to witness her suffering. It was all about her. It had always been about her.

"I can't be responsible for Mom anymore," I told Melanie. "I'm sorry, but I know that I'll never be able to get well if I'm constantly pulled down by all her negativity. I can't be around her anymore. It's just too hard for me."

"It's all right. I understand," Melanie assured me. "You need to take care of yourself. That's the most important thing right now."

"Brad isn't going to like it," I said, imagining his reaction. I called him as soon as I got off the phone with Mel.

To his credit, Brad was very supportive and understood how distraught I was over the events of the last few weeks. I told him about my newest problem and how terrible I had been feeling, and how I knew in my heart I had to distance myself from our mother or I would never have a chance to get well. He stood by my decision and said he and Mel would step into the breach. When I hung up, I felt as if the anvil was no longer on my chest.

HERE WE GO AGAIN

In July, one year after we had completed the remodel of our office condo, we closed escrow on it. This was a wonderful bit of luck for us. Not only did we have one less property to deal with, we had struck a great, mutually beneficial bargain with the buyers. Life was good.

Before I went up to Nevada City the following month, I decided to redo the grapefruit juice/olive oil torture again because it was so much fun the first time around. Nothing had changed acid-wise, so I got to thinking maybe I needed to do the treatment longer.

I did it over, with no better results the second time. I did however make two important discoveries, on the off chance I would ever try it again: use regular olive oil—*not* extra-virgin—and chug it. Sipping it only prolongs the agony.

And while I'm on the subject of *I'LL TRY ANYTHING*, I must add a few words about my experience with Superfruits. Not until after I had fallen for a sales pitch was I aware that such a concept existed.

My introduction to this highly successful realm of health-oriented marketing began with a call from my sister. She had caught me on a particularly bad day. I was lying down, doubled over in pain after having to abandon our plans of going to lunch and a movie. Had I not been in such bad shape, my natural cynicism may have kept me from falling for the con.

Mel had gotten a call from a friend of hers who had been visiting her ailing mother in Florida. She was very excited to tell Mel about this drink made from the juice of a certain cactus that had a remarkable effect on inflammation. The friend's mother had tried this juice drink and in less than a week, her orthopedic shoes were falling off her once-swollen feet. It was a miracle.

The timing of Mel's call was perfect: a miracle was exactly what I needed right about then. My spirit was at a dangerously low point; the pain was so all-encompassing, I couldn't see beyond it. Mel gave me the name of a website where I could learn more about this gift from heaven. When I was able to move again, I checked it out.

When I typed in the URL, a webpage popped up. I can't remember the last time I had seen a single webpage; it had been at least a decade. I clicked on the arrow and watched as a 45-minute testimonial began with a kindly, middle-aged woman telling the amazing story of what this cactus juice had done for her husband and dozens of others she knew.

Because of the incredible turnaround in her husband's health, they had made this video in order to "share the blessing" with others. The way they spread this blessing was by giving a bottle of this wonderful-tasting juice to people suffering from all types of crippling inflammation. All I had to do was call her number and she would determine whether I was a good candidate for this life-altering cure. If I were, I would be sent a free bottle of this magic elixir. I got on the phone immediately.

So convincing was the woman and so compromised was my brain, the fact that I didn't reach this woman personally did not raise any red flags. I got the erroneous impression a friend or neighbor was helping to man the phones.

I told my sad story to this sympathetic woman who said Lyme disease qualified me for a free bottle of this extraordinary juice. Oh, joy. The bottle would be on its way and I would probably receive it in a day or two. Oh, double joy! But it was very important to keep continuously taking this product in order to feel the maximum benefits; any downtime could result in the delay of improvement.

She recommended I purchase a case of this juice to have at the ready so I could start feeling the benefits as soon as possible. If I bought a case that day, I would be eligible to receive the discounted price of $103 instead of the regular price of $129 for a case of four bottles. Guess what I did. Open mouth, insert hook. I gave the woman my credit card information.

I received my gift two days later. It was sent next day air. I rushed home from the post office and poured myself a small glass of this beautiful, ruby red juice. It was delicious! I couldn't wait to take another dose, so I didn't. As Julie, my acupuncturist will tell you, I practice the belief that *more is more better*. It was a good thing I had ordered a case of the stuff; I couldn't stand the thought of being without this hope in a bottle.

My shipment came and I faithfully continued to drink it, waiting with anticipation for the pain to decrease. When I looked at the invoice, I discovered that I'd been charged $129—$103 plus plus. Oh well, that wasn't such a big deal, not if the stuff really worked.

Because my confidence in this juice was so high, I couldn't help thinking of all the people I knew who could benefit from the anti-inflammatory properties. But even though I was thinking along those lines, I was stunned and appalled when I received in the mail recruiting materials and a sales log.

A few days later, when I opened an envelope containing a debit card in my name, I hit the ceiling. I got on the phone with the issuer of the card and gave them holy hell. I made them cancel the card with its $100 advance on future sales immediately. My faith in the product suddenly wavered.

It was about this time that I finally put on my glasses and took a look at the list of ingredients. Naïve fool that I was, I had assumed the elixir I was quaffing was pure cactus juice. The teeny-tiny white print on the side of the bottle I mistook for praise of the nopal cactus was in fact a catalog of nearly every fruit juice known to man. Cactus extract was not high on this list.

No wonder it tasted so darn good. Now I really felt like an idiot. Seeing this product in a new light, I had serious doubts about its effectiveness as an anti-inflammatory. I decided instead to use my last two bottles as a mixer with vodka.

When confirmation of my second shipment came, I really flipped. This time when I called the number in Florida, I didn't get a sweet, compassionate soul on the other end. My indignation was met with argumentative indifference. I told the woman I had never signed up for auto-ship, and after a prolonged battle, I told her if she didn't stop the order, I would simply refuse it. I also told her I didn't want to receive another piece of junk mail, including all the motivational sales tools and the shameless monthly magazines that I promptly deposited in the recycle bin.

Despite my bad experience with the duplicitous church lady from Florida, it was hard for me to give up hope on the benefits of nopal cactus as an anti-inflammatory. I had done some research and found that pure nopal cactus extract could be bought in powder form. No fancy fruit cocktail, and it cost much less per dose. Problem was, it tasted god-awful, no matter what I tried to do to it. I finally had to admit there was no magic cure for all that ailed me. Darn. It had been so nice to hope there was.

Shortly after the cactus juice episode, I received an email from an old friend I hadn't heard from in a while. She and I had been beset with weird symptoms almost simultaneously, and had shared our various hopes and dead ends with each other over the years. She was writing to let me know about a product she had been using for several months with remarkable results.

As I read the lengthy email, I was half afraid she was going to start extolling the virtues of nopal cactus juice. But no; it was another superfruit, the mangosteen. She told me how truly miraculous her improvements had been, and how much research she had done on the product before she started using it.

I didn't doubt a word of what she was telling me; I knew her to be very practical and naturally skeptical. If it passed muster in her eyes, it had to have some merit. If I hadn't gone the cactus route, I would've jumped on the mangosteen in a nanosecond.

Aside from the fact that I was now officially off superfruits, the mangosteen marketing scheme was very similar in its concept. But unlike the sneaky approach the nopal cactus pushers used to ensnare recruits, my friend had been very upfront with the fact that she was now a mangosteen distributor.

As I would later discover, there is a vast array of superfruit hawkers out there. I saw a program on TV about how two men with a marketing plan already in place went in search of a superfruit to exploit. Apparently, it's a superfruit jungle out there.

Back at Dr. W's in August, we were disheartened to find that my blood was pure chaos again. I couldn't seem to hold a charge. Coming more frequently might've helped, but it was all I could do (and afford) to make it up every couple of months or so.

Dr. W did all the usual stuff to get my blood looking good again, including more nasal injections, which were so off-the-charts painful, I was sure they were doing more harm than good. I had several appointments while I was up there, and by the end things were looking hopeful again.

When I got back to Santa Barbara, it was time to put some of the proceeds from the sale of our office to work around the house. Once again, I rounded up the painters, the electrician, Mike the handyman, the gardeners and others to do a much-needed update on our property. Nothing too major, but what we did made a big difference. It felt good to whip the house into shape again.

I was scheduled to go back to see Dr. W in October, but the timing was bad for Melanie. I rescheduled for November. When November came, I was faced with two problems. Mel had decided she couldn't face another Nevada City winter; she was moving to Kauai, and would be over there looking for a place to live when my appointment was scheduled. And now there was no longer a direct flight from Santa Barbara to Sacramento.

Because of the difficulties in getting up to see Dr. W, I started to reevaluate the situation. I had been up for treatment five times in a little over a year. I was definitely not on death's door anymore, but other than maybe stabilizing my condition, there hadn't really been any other improvements. The truth was I had developed more problems than I had on my first visit: the constant burning from the acid and the microscopic colitis. All signs were pointing to finding another means of treatment.

It was then I started thinking about the anti-microbials I had taken under Dr. Q's supervision. I went to the site where I had purchased those products and was surprised and delighted to find that Dr. P had put a prepackaged protocol on the site that would take the user through six months of treatment.

This brought a new ray of hope to me: I would be able to receive treatment from the doctor Rachael went to in Arizona, without the travel hassle and the huge expense. It wouldn't be the same personalized care that Rachael had received, but since Dr. P had retired, that wasn't an option anyway.

What made me optimistic about this regimen was the way it differed from the first one I was on. Instead of alternating between two antimicrobial herbs every 14 days, I would be taking a total of six—five of which I had never taken before—2–3 per day. And I would be taking these doses four times a day, as opposed to only twice. It was also mandatory, in order for the protocol to be effective, to drink between 3–4 quarts of water every day.

Not having any better options at that point, I ordered the first two months of the protocol, which came with instructions and a daily, dose by dose log that made managing all the different antimicrobials and detoxifiers very easy. All these differences made me feel more confident that the antimicrobial approach would be successful this time around.

In addition to the new protocol, I decided to schedule weekly appointments with Julie. My hope was that strengthening my body while killing the Lyme would be the magic combination. Those two things, plus monthly massages from my friend Diane and visits to Dr. Brad as needed, constituted my new game plan. And hopefully all this would do the trick. It had to. It was my last best hope.

ALL IN THE FAMILY

Since my decision to break off contact with my mother, she would express to Mel and Brad her frustration, concern—and lastly—remorse over my lack of communication with her.

"I acted very badly," she finally admitted after several weeks of being incommunicado with me. It was a relief to hear she was taking responsibility for her actions. Even so, I wasn't ready to get back into the arena with her. Dead set as I was on shielding myself, I doubt I would've hung up on her if she had called. Fortunately for me, she didn't.

If I'd surrendered to my ingrained conditioning and called her in the early weeks after our last encounter, I'm sure my call would've been met with an icy reception. She would've never accepted responsibility for her bad behavior. Instead, she would've mounted an offensive heavily laden with guilt-producing barbs.

I knew my mother too well; the only way to protect myself was to sever our relationship until I felt physically and mentally up to dealing with her again.

As the months passed, my mother became genuinely sorrowful that I hadn't been in touch with her. "I just don't understand why she doesn't call me anymore." The situation was starting to wear on Brad.

One day in November, Brad called me. He had been planning on coming down with Alice, but they were in the middle of something and couldn't get away after all. We chatted for a while, then he got around to the real reason for his call.

Though I had sought and received his blessing to take myself out of the equation, Brad was now feeling the strain of having to field questions about me. He didn't like the chasm between his mother and his sister, which I can understand. But I thought he understood I had only cut off contact in order to protect myself.

Alas, Brad was no longer sympathetic to my situation. I tried to explain how important it was to me to have the freedom to save my sanity and take care of my health. We went around and around, covering the same turf, getting nowhere. We had come to an impasse, and I didn't know how to give Brad what he wanted.

"Can't you just call her?" he asked.

"Brad, I'm not ready to do that," I tried to explain. "It's not a good time for me right now."

"I'm just having a problem with the fact that you've disowned our mother," he spat, each word loaded with venom.

"I haven't disowned her—"

"You've disowned our mother," he repeated forcefully.

"Brad," I choked, "I have to go now." I hung up the phone and burst into tears. *Why did he have to do this to me?* We had talked about my decision at length, a decision that was very hard for me to come to, but one that was absolutely necessary. I had been taking care of her for the 12 years she had lived in Santa Barbara; did I really have to put her wellbeing ahead of mine forever?

Now I had a problem with two out of three members of my family. I must really be a shit. But I was going to remain true to myself, for once in my life, and put my needs before others. If I didn't, I wouldn't have a hope of getting better.

Two days before Thanksgiving, after I had cleaned the house and was lying down, I said to myself, *I think I'll give Mom a call.* Before I reached for the phone, another voice asked, *are you sure you're ready??* I thought carefully about what I was proposing to do for a moment and decided, *yeah, I'm ready.*

As soon as my mom heard my voice, she perked up. Without going into any of the events that led up to my lengthy absence in her life, we just seemed to pick up more or less where we'd left off, with one notable difference.

During the five-month hiatus in our relationship, my mother had gone through a very dramatic change. I could hear it in her voice, in the questions she asked me, in the way she spoke of the things in her life. There was a stark lack of bitterness toward the world in general.

When I asked how she was feeling, she laughed lightly and made a noncommittal remark, brushing off her aches and pains and trials as being a part of everyday life that were hardly worth mentioning, instead of making them out to be the bane of her existence.

This was a huge about-face for her. Her ailments had been the primary focus of her life for decades; it had been impossible for her to see past them, and they prevented her from recognizing the good in her life.

I told her about the new treatment plan I had started. I told her we were having Josiah, Justine and the kids over for Thanksgiving dinner. I didn't extend an invitation because my mother hadn't accepted one for either Thanksgiving or Christmas in many years. Or if she did accept, she would make herself sick from stress and cancel at the last minute.

There seemed no need to go through that charade, and I was pleased I didn't feel compelled to include her, knowing I would only be rebuffed. I had learned how to spare us both from that kind of situation.

We talked for about forty minutes. Toward the end of the conversation, when I was running out of things to say, I casually wondered out loud when we would get to see Brad and Alice again. I was stunned to find out Brad had left Santa Barbara that morning.

"Brad was here?" I asked, completely flabbergasted.

"It was just a really quick trip," my mother said, trying to make light of the fact that Brad had driven down 500 miles and had not even let me know he was coming. "He got here on Saturday afternoon. He watched football all day on Sunday, then we did errands all day yesterday." *Brad was here; he didn't call; he watched football all day???*

I felt a little sting when I realized how big a rift there was between Brad and me, but then I had to laugh at the childishness of what he had done. Instead of acting like an adult and calling me to let me know he was coming, he opted for nursing his grudge and sleeping on my mom's sofa instead of having a nice, comfy guestroom and bath to himself. Not to mention some good food. *Serves him right,* I thought.

Before we hung up, my mother told me how happy she was that I had called her. She said she loved me very much and I told her I loved her too. When I hung up the phone, I felt lighter; I had made a very difficult decision to break off contact with my mother in order to save myself, and I had recognized when I was ready to reengage with her. I hadn't let anyone bully me into doing something that didn't feel right for me. These were two very big breakthroughs for me.

Had I known I could change the dynamic of our relationship and make it a healthier one for both of us, I would've done it years earlier. But the good news was we now had a more affectionate and respectful bond than we'd ever had before.

Despite the drama and the heartache, I had accomplished what I needed to and was now on a better footing with my mother and able to imagine making contact with her again. It all felt good. Except for the goofiness with Brad.

As soon as I hung up, I called Mel. I told her the shocking news that I had called Mom, and that Brad had made a sneak trip down here. She was stunned by both revelations—happy that I'd called our mother and perplexed about Brad's weird behavior. They lived next door to each other, so he had been very sneaky about his plans.

As we were howling over his devious actions, Mel got another call. It was Brad. He was calling from Roseville, wondering if she needed anything from Trader Joe's. He confessed he'd been to Santa Barbara. Mel said she knew; I had just told her. Brad put two and two together and laughed sheepishly. *Busted.*

COUNTING DOWN

The new protocol I started in November was an exercise in coordination and organization. Our kitchen counter was littered with bottles and jars, all containing potions which had to be taken at specific times with other specific herbal formulas in four ounces of water, in separate glasses, as some of the formulas were not compatible with others.

I spent a great deal of time counting out 30 drops of this, 20 of that, 10 of three others, plus the capsules. I took the first dose at least 30 minutes before breakfast; the second at least 20 minutes after the first and 20 minutes before breakfast; the third before lunch; the fourth before dinner; and the last of the day before bed. And between all these doses, I had to somehow drink an additional 6 sixteen-ounce glasses of water.

If I never needed to leave the house, this program wouldn't have been so difficult. But making sure I took my doses at the appointed times meant I would often have to mix a "to go" dose on the way out the door.

The real complicating factor was not so much about what was going in, but what needed to come out. Because I was drinking almost a gallon of water a day—and I didn't dare drink anything else—I learned the location of every restroom in my vicinity. Every activity had to be planned out so I would be within range of one, if needed. Had I been working, I probably could've been fired for so much time away from my post.

Besides overworking my bladder, each dose produced a "die off" reaction, which invariably made me feel extra horrible. Twenty minutes after every dose, the pain would ratchet up from almost tolerable to severe, making me moan and writhe, if I was at liberty to do so.

But none of the drawbacks mattered to me; I was determined to get through this protocol, for I was now certain this plan was going to work. When the six months were over, I was going to be well. I was convinced I was on the right track now. Finally.

Even though I was experiencing the Herxheimer's reaction for the better part of every day, I was noticing one area of improvement. It was something I had first gotten a mere hint of after we moved back into Summerland, and it had been so random and short-lived, I didn't know what to make of it.

But now I was receiving these incremental flashes more often, moments when I would have this feeling of wellbeing come over me, like a flashback, that would transport me back in time, and I could remember what I used to feel like before I got sick.

During these tiny bursts of physical memory, I would actually feel the hope, excitement and verve that had been the essence of my being in the years prior to Lyme. Those snapshots not only thrilled me, but gave me hope I was coming back to myself. At the risk of sounding airy-fairy, it felt as though my spirit was returning.

A good example of the occasional glimpses I'd have of my former self was during a walk I took in the wooded area behind our house. I was bounding down the trail and I became aware of a peculiar lightness—lightness in my step and in my frame of mind. I had the feeling I used to get when I was out walking, that feeling of knowing I could depend on my body to take me anywhere I wanted to go. I was alone, just the clothes on my back, but I felt as though I could take on anything that came my way. It was me in my pure essence.

By the time I got home, I was in pain again. But that brief stroll through my former wellbeing gave me a precious hope that I held onto tightly.

January 12th is a special day for me. It's a day I always acknowledge and celebrate privately. It marks the anniversary of the day I moved to Santa Barbara back in 1979. That move completely changed the course of my life. For me it was the real beginning of my life as I know it now.

January 12, 2011 was a gorgeous day. There was a low tide in the morning, which I took advantage of. On my way back to the car, I ran into Guy. He told me about a phone call he'd just gotten from a realtor up in Santa Ynez. The realtor had a client who he'd been working with for over a year who hadn't found anything she liked yet. She inquired specifically about our property, having been there years before we bought it.

The realtor did some research, discovering it was our property now. As he and Guy were well acquainted, he called and picked Guy's brain. We had put the ranch up for sale, but had taken it off the market when property values began to decline.

Guy was very frank with the realtor; he told him it could be purchased, but only for a certain price. To preempt the haggling, Guy told him to show his client the property, as it had changed a lot since she'd last seen it.

The next day, Guy got another call. The woman fell in love with our ranch and was prepared to give us our price. We opened escrow after the long weekend. It was an all cash offer with no contingencies. We barely had enough time to get our clothes, art and personal effects out before the escrow closed. Everything else we left for the new owner. The buyer, a very sweet woman, was delighted with the deal. Escrow closed in just two weeks, on February Ist.

This was one of those situations that make you wonder how you got so lucky. Guy had made the decision to put Woodstock on the market 18 months earlier, though I was worried he'd regret giving it up. When the market turned and we canceled the listing, we sort of put the property out of our minds.

We had not spent the night there since July of 2009, and now that we were back into the routine of living in Summerland, we realized we didn't feel the burning desire to be up in the valley like we used to. To have a buyer who appreciated our property as much as we did was a Godsend for us. It was truly one of those win-win-win situations.

With Woodstock sold, our lives had really come full circle, especially for me. Summerland was our only residence and I was working from home again. No more mortgage company; no more Palm Springs rental; no more apartment; no more ranch. Except for battling Lyme disease, the year could've been 1994.

Since the move back into Summerland in April 2009, I had been working on fine-tuning *Golden State*. But I had a major glitch to deal with. Two-thirds of the way through the first draft, my computer had gone berserk right before it croaked, corrupting the last third of the book. I had tried everything I could think of to remove the bizarre, unsolicited editorial corrections that the program had arbitrarily inserted. I even had an IT person try to sort it out, to no avail.

In the end, the only thing for me to do was to save the first two-thirds and rewrite the last third. I was able to do this by printing the bad pages and copying them by hand. This meant typing approx. 45,000 words over again, something that took months because of how insubordinate my hands had become.

Once that was done, I set about writing a screenplay of the book. Guy had given me the software as a birthday present, and after watching the demo, I was raring to go. Though it was something new and challenging, I really enjoyed it.

The problem was, even after severe culling, I had already used up two hours of screen time with only one quarter of the book. The only way this could work as a screenplay was as a miniseries. I had to face that after working on it for six-months, it just wasn't going to fly. Oh, well. On to the next book.

But as I was about to launch into another project, I received orders from some bossy part of my brain I never knew existed. The mandate from this self-appointed dictator was that no new book could be started until *a)* I reedited *Golden State* and drafted a query and synopsis to be sent out to agents, and *b)* I did the same for *Alligators*. Until those two projects had been groomed and submitted to literary agents, no new book could be written.

Finally, *c)*, the biggest sticking point, was that I must first write an account of the past 14 years—i.e., the Lyme madness and the unexpected upside of becoming a writer.

I must admit I consider myself a fairly disciplined person. I'm organized and task-oriented. I run a clean ship and I take personal maintenance seriously. Why all of the sudden did I need some unwelcome drill sergeant telling me what I could and couldn't do? Why the sudden mutiny in my brain?

I guess some part of my consciousness realized there really isn't any reason to continue writing books if I'm not going to do anything with them. Okay, I understand this. I owe it to the books themselves to try to get them published. But why is it necessary to write a book about myself, my experiences? I couldn't think of a more boring prospect. If I had no interest in my own story, who else would?

This is a question I'm still wondering about. That bossy voice in my brain was intimidating enough to get me to thinking seriously about the idea and to take it all the way to the conclusion. But why? I can't count it as a cathartic experience, for I wasn't in need of that.

I will say it has been an interesting journey into the past, and I suppose I've gained some hindsight in the process. Maybe when it's all done and I'm out there in cyberspace trying to hock it with my other wares I'll understand why it was so damn important to write this book.

In any event, on February 1st, 2011, two years to the date that I finished *Golden State,* I started working on this endeavor. I will get it done, figure out what—if anything—I've got, and take it from there. But I'm getting ahead of myself...

Three and a half months into the new protocol, I started noticing another change. One Saturday, I did my usual chores: work out, laundry, change the sheets, pedicure. Then Guy and I went for a long walk, had lunch and saw a movie. On the way home, around five o'clock, we went grocery shopping. Sounds like just a typical Saturday, right? Not for me.

When we were putting the groceries away, it occurred to both of us that I had been going since 7a.m. without a pause: no rest, no pain medicine, nothing. This was a major breakthrough. When I went upstairs to lie down, I did not become overwhelmed with pain, the way I normally did. The stuff was working! I could hardly believe it. But the mere absence of pain—something I had only briefly experienced a couple times in 13 years—was all the proof I needed.

For three and a half weeks, I felt good. Really good. It took my breath away when I thought about it. It was conceivable that I was going to get well and this whole crazy chapter in my life would come to an end. I would be like my old self again, full of energy and capable of doing everything I wanted to do. I was ecstatic.

But unfortunately, the tide turned again.

CAN'T WIN FOR LOSING, PART II

In mid-March, Brad and Alice came down for my mother's 81st birthday. As usual, Guy was on the spring trail ride, so it was just the three of us the first night. The following night we had reservations for dinner at my mom's favorite restaurant. Josiah and Justine arranged for a babysitter and would be joining us.

The day after Brad and Alice arrived, I woke up to several piles of cat barf. As soon as I cleaned those up, I had more to contend with. I couldn't understand what was making our cat so sick; he had been fine the night before, but now he couldn't stop vomiting.

In the afternoon, while Brad and Alice were at my mom's, I tried to get a little writing in. The cat was keeping me company in the family room. Suddenly, he jumped up and started retching. Since I had already cleaned up copious amounts of cat vomit, I quickly slid a newspaper under him right before he spewed again. Now I was getting really worried.

Not knowing what was causing the problem, I took him outside, thinking that eating some grass might settle his stomach. It was a cold, dreary day, and as soon as I set him on the lawn, it started to rain. Like most cats, ours only likes water on his terms; rain doesn't qualify. When he didn't make a mad dash for the house, I knew something must really be wrong with him.

I took him inside and put him down on a kitchen rug because his feet were wet. I then ran upstairs and got on my computer. It was 2:12 on a Saturday afternoon and I knew I'd be lucky to find a vet still opened. I called the closest one. The person who answered said they closed at 2:00, but they were taking care of another emergency. After I explained what was going on, he told me to come on over.

When I went downstairs to get the kitty, he was standing exactly where I had left him five minutes earlier. He looked so weak and sick, it almost broke my heart. Before I could get him in the carrier, he threw up twice. By the time we got to the vet's he was limp.

While we waited, the vet tech took his vitals. The doctor came in, did an exam and took him in for x-rays. They brought him back with a partially shaved neck and front leg. Because he was so dehydrated, they shot him full of fluids. Unfortunately, the vet needed to send us to a 24-hour hospital to have an ultrasound done.

At the hospital, after the test was done, there was still uncertainty about his condition. Either he had acute pancreatitis or kidney failure, the latter being fatal. In any event, he needed to stay overnight so they could keep him on fluids. It would be the first time he had ever spent the night away from home.

While waiting at the first hospital, I sent a text to Brad and Guy to let them know what was going on. While I was in waiting room at the second hospital, Guy walked in. He had left the trail ride early; his horse was outside in the trailer. He sat with me while I waited to speak to the vet, then left to put Dixie up.

When I was finally back in my car, I called Brad. I was pretty frazzled. I told him I didn't think I could pull myself together in time for our dinner reservations. He understood.

While I was talking to him, Josiah called. Their sitter had flaked out. I told him not to worry about it; I wouldn't be going either. He was sorry to hear about the kitty; he was the one who had found him 12 years earlier at an abandoned house. I hung up with Josiah and cried the rest of the way home, not knowing if I'd ever see our sweet cat again.

The following month was a rollercoaster ride. I can't remember how many vet visits there were, but there were at least two or three every week. There was another trip to an emergency veterinary hospital in Ventura on another Saturday when his symptoms suddenly changed and the opposite end started acting unpredictably. His belly was shaved and another test was performed.

This time the vet wasn't sure if it was Inflammatory Bowel Disease or Lymphoma. After seven hours down there and two confabs with the vet, I decided that if he had lymphoma, he was going to die and there was no reason to put him through any more hell. They wanted to keep him over night because he was dehydrated and not eating. I couldn't do that to him again. I told the doctor to give him a water hump; he was coming home with us.

During the two weeks that followed, I took him back to the first vet numerous times. We decided to treat for IBD, since that was our best hope. The treatment for this was prednisone, antibiotics and a new diet, but the vet was hesitant about initiating the protocol. His symptoms continued. Guy took him in one Saturday when I was preparing for company, but he was sent home with the same food and no injection.

I was up all night with the kitty as his body rebelled. Neither one of us slept. It was torture for both of us. The next morning I got him in to see another vet. She gave him an injection and sent us home with a prescription.

Our kitty was back to his old self in a matter of days. If I had gone there in the first place, we could've all been spared a lot of grief. But animal health is really no different than it is for humans; despite all the advances, so much of it is still trial and error.

Because of all the cat drama, the respite from pain was short-lived. Now I was just as bad off as I'd ever been. By this time, it was late April. I was leaving for Kauai in a few days to celebrate Mel's 50th birthday. Though I was in bad shape, I kept myself going with the thought of seven days of rest and relaxation.

The trip wasn't quite as laid back as I'd hoped. In the space of a week, I unpacked and repacked four times, as circumstances had us moving from one location to another. I also had the constraints and pitfalls of the Lyme protocol to deal with. Now the hope lay in getting home and getting back into a good routine.

It was clear to me now I wouldn't be well when the six months of treatment were up. Instead of quitting in late May, I ordered eight more weeks' worth of antimicrobials.

On June 19th, Father's Day, I forgot to take my second dose before we went to brunch. I took it as soon as we got home. 20 minutes later, I was wracked with pain.

It hit me as I lay there, every fiber of my body resonating with pain, that maybe I'd killed enough Lyme. I couldn't see the sense in putting myself through several more weeks of die-off symptoms. I decided to stop the protocol.

The next day, I felt much better. As far as I was concerned, feeling better was more important at that point than trying to get better. I was back to the "do nothing" approach, but it was a tremendous relief to be out of that cycle.

Around the same time, I decided I really needed to find out if this acid problem was causing any permanent damage. Out of desperation, I had been back to see Dr. J. His advice was to go to UCLA. He could give me the name of a specialist who was on the forefront of dealing with IBS.

But I didn't want to go down to UCLA; it was too far away and I didn't feel like being a human guinea pig. Besides, I didn't really think that IBS was my problem. I got the message that Dr. J was pretty much through dealing with me, so I decided a new doctor was in order, regardless.

Acting on the advice of my friend Diane, I checked out a doctor she had seen down in Ventura. I liked what I read about him online and made an appointment. I was fortunate to get a cancelation the following day, which I was grateful for. Not only would I not have to wait weeks to see him, but I wouldn't have time to fret over what dealing with a new doctor would be like.

It had been years since I had auditioned for a new doctor and I found myself quite nervous. In the space of 24 hours, I had already worked up a good deal of trepidation. Would this new doctor be indifferent? Would he treat me like I had nothing better to do than waste doctors' time? Would he come to the same conclusion as Dr. J, that there was really nothing wrong with me?

With all these fledgling worries floating around in my head, I drove down to Ventura, got lost and had a succession of meltdowns before I finally arrived at the doctor's office 15 minutes late.

As I sat there in the small, windowless room, breathing in the same stale air as the patient before me, I tried to brace myself for the worst. I had read on this doctor's bio that he spoke four languages, including Russian, which both impressed and intimidated me.

When I finally heard the doorknob turn forty-five minutes later, I had convinced myself the man I was about to see was going to spend a total of twelve and a half minutes with me and send me away with the same diagnosis, or otherwise flat out dismiss me as a loony.

When Dr. Z entered the room, I went limp with relief.

"*Sooo* sorry to keep you waiting on this absolutely beautiful day! And I'm sure you'd rather be anywhere other than here," he said wistfully, as he slunk into the room. I had told Diane I wanted a doctor as smart as House and as kind as Wilson. Dr. Z's credentials said smart; his demeanor said gentle as a lamb. He was a cross between my Uncle Richard and Mr. Rogers. My prayers had been answered.

Dr. Z took a seat at his computer and finished inputting my data himself. While he logged the answers, I took stock of him: the pale purple shirt and wild pink and purple tie, the curly, flyaway hair, the slouchy posture, the small spitball on his smiling lower lip. *This is my kind of doctor.*

After he got my data entered, we got down to the interview process. I told him about the incessant acid problem that had been raging for over a year and a half. I told him about Dr. J's diagnosis and recommendation. I told him about the Lyme. I told him of all the different treatments I had tried in an attempt to get rid of the problem and how the symptoms stayed stubbornly the same.

Dr. Z thoughtfully considered everything I told him. We discussed different methods of determining acid production. We talked about doing another endoscopy. Because of the Lyme, he wondered if I possibly had a rare esophageal disease. We talked about treatment, if I did indeed have this disease, which didn't seem so far-fetched, considering the microscopic colitis and the sphenoid sinus disease, both of which are fairly uncommon.

In the end, we decided to schedule the endoscopy, during which he could take a biopsy and rule in or out other conditions. There was one small catch: our Cobra insurance had run out the day before and our new insurance kicked in that day, but we wouldn't have any documentation for a few weeks. I would need at least a policy number before we could schedule the procedure.

The irony of all this insurance hoopla is that not one Lyme-related doctor's visit or treatment has been paid by insurance. Everything, including the IGeneX test to determine if I had the disease, had been paid out of our pockets. I don't ever want to know how much that adds up to, but I know it would run into the tens of thousands.

So, the plan with Dr. Z was to wait to schedule the endoscopy until after I had all the insurance info. I was really ready to get this behind me, but we now had another glitch. Even before the insurance cards arrived, Guy became covered by his new employer. We cancelled our outrageously expense coverage and waited for the newest insurance cards. Three months later, I was still waiting.

Guy was able to at least get our policy number online, but by then I was feeling inertia about the whole thing. I still had the problem, but I kept hoping the various new remedies I'd been trying would bring about a change.

It's hard to believe, but like all the other pains I'd been toting around for years, I'd more or less become accustomed to the constant burning. I decided to put the endoscopy on hold, indefinitely.

The Upside to the Downside

The new freedom that came from not being enslaved to the complicated antimicrobial regimen felt incredibly liberating. I could eat whenever I was hungry without first having to take a dose, then waiting. I could go out and about without running to the nearest restroom every 30 minutes. I was off the strict diet that made eating a challenge.

I was still in pain, but not as much as when I was killing Lyme. I felt as though Lyme was no longer holding my head under water. If I could keep that stalemate going, I'd consider myself improved.

After about a month of feeling relatively decent, Lyme upped the ante. All of a sudden, every joint hurt—elbows, knees, neck, shoulders, hip, hands, feet—in a way that was different than before. When I wake up in the morning, my hands are so sore and stiff, I actually have to peel my fingers open. It takes a few minutes of exercises before I can use them.

In November 2011, I finally decided I needed to make sure the constant acid reflux wasn't causing a serious threat of esophageal cancer. It had been going on for two solid years. I called Dr. Z's office and scheduled the endoscopy.

The procedure itself was more comfortable than my previous two. I was allowed to keep my clothes on and the nurse wrapped me in warm blankets. I was able to speak with the doctor before the scope and asked him specifically what he'd be taking biopsies for.

When the procedure was over and I had come to, Dr. Z told me his findings. There was evidence of lesions in the stomach wall and the esophagus; he would know the cause when the lab report came back. I was given pictures taken from the endoscopy and a written report listing areas of concern and possible diagnoses.

A week later, he called and told me the biopsies were negative for H. Pylori and Barrett's Esophagus, a precursor to cancer. His conclusion was mild GERD. I asked him if the amount of pain I had been experiencing for two years had only caused minor erosion, did he think continued acid reflux would ever develop into cancer? He thought not.

He suspected the inordinate burning sensation might be due to further nerve damage, and suggested I see an ear-nose-throat specialist. He also prescribed the only protease pump inhibitor I had never taken. He said it would take a couple weeks for it to start working. I took it for one month, with no results. Since it didn't make any difference, I decided not to refill the prescription; there wasn't any point. I opted instead for taking aloe vera juice, which supposedly heals internal burns.

If I'm not in any danger of developing cancer from the burning, then I'd just as soon stay away from pharmaceuticals. If it's just another inroad for Lyme disease, no drug is going to do any good, anyway. I know I must take up the Lyme battle again, but it's hard to muster the requisite fortitude.

My Lyme offensive now consists of having weekly acupuncture treatments and sporadically combing the web for possible tips on how to combat the various problems I'm still wrangling with. Even though I'm still mostly avoiding traditional medicine, simply because it has nothing to offer me at this point, I prefer to get my info from the medical-based sites.

One inspired attempt led me to discover that acupuncture and B-12 are recommended for people with peripheral neuropathy. That was encouraging. I already had the acupuncturist. I told Julie of my findings, and now she uses micro-current to treat the nerve damage. The B-12 was easy enough to get my hands on; I now stick a patch behind my ear once a week, just in case it will do some good.

It's sometimes hard to know if anything I try has any real benefit. I don't know if the improvements are so incremental that I don't notice them, or if the sum of all the crazy, weird, and just plain dubious methods I've tried have in some small way brought me to this point where I don't feel like road kill every minute of my life.

As I look back at this record of the last 14 years of grasping at straws, it occurs to me that, except for a few truly disinterested and useless physicians, most of the healthcare professionals I've dealt with have given me at least one puzzle piece to find a home for.

With Dr. Q, it was emphasis on diet and supplements like omega-3. Dr. W stressed the importance of proper blood and energy flow—*Blockage leads to stagnation, in which bacteria collects, which in turn creates disease*—and believed in making the body stronger so that it could take care of disease on its own.

Dr. F got me started on sleeping with a pillow between my knees to relieve the pain in my hips. Dr. Brad put my bones back where they belong. Julie keeps my *qi* flowing and my pulses strong. Dr. V introduced me to hyperbaric oxygen chambers, which did make me feel better for a time.

Maybe I wouldn't be doing as well, relatively speaking, if I hadn't been through this maze of treatments. Maybe each step strengthened me a bit, and maybe it all was necessary to get me to this stage.

I have to confess I no longer believe I can be freed of this disease; that hope died after the last antimicrobial protocol. But the good news is I don't feel completely devastated by this realization. Late-stage Lyme is nearly impossible to cure. There's only so much I can do to fight it. But I'm not giving up.

I've been slugging it out for almost five years now, trying my damnedest to kill the bastard. Now I'm hoping Dr. W is right, and that if I'm a really good girl and take extra good care of myself, *someday* I might feel just a little bit better, maybe shake off a couple symptoms. That's all I'm hoping for these days.

When I was first diagnosed with Lyme, Dr. Mesipam told me about a patient of his who had also been diagnosed with the disease. She, too, had been struggling for years to find out what was wrong with her, and consequently, she also had late-stage Lyme. She had chosen the traditional route: PICC lines and heavy-duty antibiotics. When I had asked how she was doing, Dr. M said she was feeling better after six months of treatment.

Just recently, I found out that after 5 years this same woman is still on antibiotics and not doing well at all. It's horrible to think what she must be going through. But it also makes me feel like I didn't make a mistake by not going down that path. I may not be well, but I do feel better than I did a year ago. Sort of.

A lot has transpired in the 14 years that I've been struggling with my health. There have been many times when I thought the future looked pretty grim.

Often while lying down in the apartment I would contrast my symptoms and the way I felt with my mom's condition. She had many health problems over the years, including breast cancer. Despite her assorted health problems, I sometimes felt that she would outlive me. I couldn't imagine where I would ever find the strength to carry on past the age of 50.

Even though I was only in my forties at the time, I found it hard to imagine that I'd ever be released from my unnamed hell. One event sums up my doubts about my future: it was finding out that Justine was pregnant with Dash.

When I heard this wonderful news, I was very happy. But it hit me I would never be the grandmother I wanted to be. I knew it would be difficult to participate fully in Dash's life. It made me feel hollow inside to think I would be the invalid grandmother who wasn't able to play a significant part in his childhood, a shadowy figure Dash would barely remember.

When we got the good news about Milli's eventually arrival, I became hopeful. I had been diagnosed by that time and was on Dr. Q's protocol, and firmly believed I would get well. Now I was able to think of myself as a real grandmother, one who could get on the ground and play with the grandkids, or pick them up when they came running to me. I was delighted at the thought of having two grandchildren.

On January 11, 2010, I became a grandmother three times over with the birth of Stella Pearl. I love being a grandmother and thank my lucky stars I'm at least stable enough to act like a grandmother when the opportunity arises. I'm going to do my damnedest to make sure I'll be able to spend time with them and live out happy moments we can remember forever.

The other thing that makes me feel good right now is knowing that as soon as this tale is told, I am free to write anything my heart desires. I'm looking forward to digging into a great big, juicy novel. I've had several ideas auditioning in the friendlier part of my brain. It'll only be a matter of deciding which one to go with first.

Since I started writing this account, I've taken the bold step of publishing online. I've given up on researching agents and sending out queries and collecting rejections. I've opted instead for trying to take my books directly to readers. I figure I have nothing to lose by trying. Maybe something good will come of this.

In the meantime, I'll keep up the good fight against the Lyme, and keep writing like it really matters.

A couple of months ago, as I was walking upstairs to bed, I detoured to my office, where I sat down and wrote a song. I hadn't done that in many years. As I read the lyrics, I smiled to myself; *well, well—look who's back*. A week later, I made the same detour and wrote another song.

I guess it's time to find out what Tobias is up to now...